HEALTHCARE MARKETING

STRATEGIES FOR CREATING VALUE IN THE PATIENT EXPERIENCE

FIRST EDITION

BARBARA ROSS WOOLDRIDGE AND KERRI M. CAMP

Bassim Hamadeh, CEO and Publisher
Bob Farrell, Senior Field Acquisitions Editor
Gem Rabanera, Project Editor
Chritian Berk, Associate Production Editor
Miguel Macias, Senior Graphic Designer
Trey Soto, Licensing Coordinator
Chris Snipes, Interior Designer
Natalie Piccotti, Senior Marketing Manager
Kassie Graves, Vice President of Editorial
Jamie Giganti, Director of Academic Publishing

Cover image copyright © 2017 by iStockphoto LP / TethysImagingLLC.

Printed in the United States of America.

ISBN: 978-1-5165-1426-7 (pbk) / 978-1-5165-1427-4 (br)

TABLE OF CONTENTS

CHAPTER 1: THE 7PS OF HEALTHCARE ORGANIZATIONS

CHAPTER 2: THE HEALTHCARE PARADIGM SHIFT

CHAPTER 3: UNDERSTANDING THE COMPETITIVE ENVIRONMENT

CHAPTER 4: STRATEGIC HEALTHCARE MARKETING

CHAPTER 5: CREATING VALUE BY LISTENING

CHAPTER 6: HOW CAREGIVERS CREATE VALUE

CHAPTER 7: BEING PATIENT-CENTERED—A KEY FOR SUCCESS

CHAPTER 8: ETHICS AND HEALTHCARE MARKETING

ACKNOWLEDGMENTS

A number of individuals contributed to this book. We would like to thank Carroll Rogé, Paula E. Anthony, Felix Liu, John Rathnam, John Frank Harper, East Texas Medical Center, Patrick Simonson, and Beth Israel Deaconess Medical Center Ethics program for their contributions to the notes from practice. We would also like to thank Kerrie Anne Ambort-Clark and Brandy Meadows for their contributions of case studies. We also would like to thank our editors at Cognella, Gem Rabanera and Bob Farrell, for having faith in this project.

Each of us would like to add a personal note:

(From Barbara Woolridge) I would like to thank my wonderful husband Stan Wooldridge and my sweet son Ford for allowing me the time without guilt to work on this project. I want to add it was a pleasure to work with such a wonderful co-author as Kerri Camp.

(From Kerri Camp) First of all, I want to thank my loving and supportive husband Danny Camp for his continual encouragement. I also want to thank my students for challenging me to write a textbook that meets their desire to learn more about marketing as it relates to the healthcare field. Finally, I would like to thank my co-author Barbara Ross Wooldridge for partnering with me on this project.

PREFACE

Healthcare is a dynamic and changing industry. It is no longer enough to be a "good" clinician. Those involved in healthcare face the dual challenges of being strong in both healthcare expertise and management. The Affordable Healthcare Act has moved patient satisfaction to the forefront of healthcare. Irrespective of any forthcoming changes to healthcare legislation, the horse is out of the barn, and patient satisfaction will not go away—nor will the measurement of patient satisfaction.

The rapidly changing environment creates new challenges that must be solved. Kate Walsh, president and CEO of Boston Medical Center, stated at the sixth annual Becker's Hospital Review, "The biggest [surprise] is just how hard it is to move our patient satisfaction scores. Our other one is just how slow the rate of change actually is, despite how breathless we all feel." Hence, this book was developed to provide insight on how healthcare combined with marketing principles can help healthcare providers not only survive in this volatile environment but thrive.

This text provides the foundation of marketing and its role in healthcare in a unique and focused manner. Highlights of this book include insights from the practice of healthcare professionals on the front line of this changing world, focused readings on key topics, and background on marketing insights deeply connected to the world of healthcare.

1
CHAPTER

THE 7Ps OF HEALTHCARE ORGANIZATIONS

LEARNING OBJECTIVES

In this chapter, you will learn about the following:

- The 7Ps of the marketing mix
- Target markets
- Value proposition
- Perceptions about branding
- The marketing mindset
- Importance of building trusting and lasting relationships with patients

The last three learning objectives will be discussed in the reading selection "Marketing for Doctors and Staff" (Stevens, 2015).

INTRODUCTION

The purpose of marketing is to identify the wants and needs of consumers and then to develop the appropriate marketing mix that will communicate that value for consumers. The American Marketing Association (AMA, July 2013) offers the following definition: "Marketing is the activity, set of institutions, and processes for creating, communicating, delivering, and exchanging offerings that have value for customers, clients, partners, and society at large."

Although many marketers use the 4Ps of the marketing mix—Product, Price, Place, and Promotion—healthcare delivery, due to its services nature, encompasses several other aspects. For this reason, the 7Ps of Creating Value provided in figure 1.2 are more appropriate for healthcare organizations. All of the seven components of the marketing mix are controllable variables for the healthcare organization. The marketing mix is also a means for healthcare organizations to differentiate themselves from other competitors in the healthcare environment. The competitive landscape will be discussed in greater detail in chapter 3.

NOTES FROM PRACTICE

Figure 1.1 Carroll Rogé

Carroll Rogé never planned to pursue a career in healthcare marketing. "I liked to write, so I gravitated toward journalism and technical writing in college," he remembers. "My first job out of school was as a writer at an engineering firm, where I worked with their ad agency. I learned quickly that marketing was creative and fun for me."

From there, Rogé moved on to direct the advertising program for a chain of sporting goods stores. "I enjoyed that, but I really missed having a connection with people and telling their stories," Rogé says.

Rogé ultimately accepted a position in marketing for the ETMC Regional Healthcare System, based in Tyler, Texas. "It was very fulfilling to tell the stories of life-saving care that make a profound difference in the lives of patients and their families."

Enjoying being able to write again, Rogé became ETMC's corporate director of marketing and pursued his MBA at night. In this role, he directed the promotion and outreach for the healthcare system operating in 40 counties of northeast Texas.

Currently, he serves as vice president of marketing and planning for the organization. He also spearheads its customer service program.

Rogé sums up his thoughts best, "I'm thankful to go home most days feeling good about the people I've touched. I wasn't cut out to be caregiver, but I enjoy supporting our amazing healthcare team and helping fulfill our mission of care. Unlike any other type of marketing, working in healthcare is incredibly rewarding. I'm glad I found where I was supposed to be."

7Ps FOR CREATING VALUE

The 7Ps of Creating Value model (figure 1.2) identifies the seven areas healthcare organizations should examine when determining whether the products and services offered provide value to their patients. The specific areas that should be explored within each of the 7Ps are discussed below.

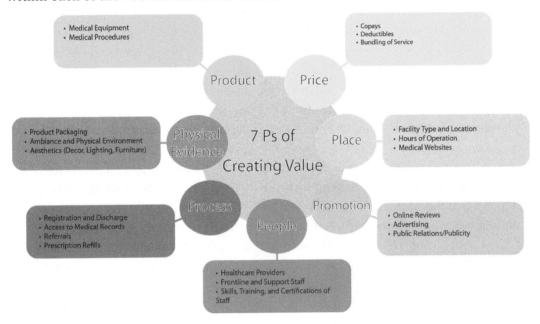

Figure 1.2 7Ps of Creating Value

1. PRODUCT

Product includes the goods, services, or ideas that are offered by the organization to consumers. Typically in healthcare today, a product refers to the medical procedure delivered by the *provider or facility* or the medical equipment or pharmaceuticals sold to the consumers for their personal use. Hospital patients are surveyed as part of the Affordable Care Act with the standardized Hospital Consumer Assessment of Healthcare Providers and Systems (HCAHPS) survey that is administered by third-party vendors. Because the entire patient experience encompasses many different areas of the hospital—including registration, emergency department, surgery staff, floor nurses, phlebotomy personnel, hospitalists, surgeons, and primary care providers, to name a few—the patient's evaluation of the services received may be difficult for healthcare administrators to effectively assess and manage.

2. PRICE

Price refers to the amount consumers are willing to pay for their medical procedure, medical equipment, or pharmaceuticals. Within healthcare, the concept of price is even more complex due to the many types of reimbursement. For example, patients may have commercial insurance (Blue Cross Blue Shield, United, Aetna, etc.), Medicare, Medicaid, Veterans Administration, workers' compensation, or private pay (uninsured). Medical procedures may be bundled with anesthesiology, radiology, laboratory services, or other hospital services, or procedures may be billed separately to the consumer.

This issue becomes even more difficult to understand when providers factor in the value-based modifier that is now tied to reimbursements. This will be discussed in greater depth in chapters 5 and 6. One aspect providers should control is the transparency of pricing. If a patient has scheduled an outpatient surgical procedure with a surgeon, the surgeon's staff should preauthorize the procedure with the patient's insurance, determine the portion of the deductible the patient has or has not met, and estimate the out-of-pocket expenses the patient can expect to pay from that provider. The patient should also be notified to expect other charges from the hospital and hospital providers. All of these communications should be documented in writing and signed by the patient prior to the scheduled surgical procedure. Obviously, in the event of emergency procedures, this may not be possible. However, with planned procedures, the expectation by consumers is that providers should be able to closely estimate what the patient should expect to pay so that necessary arrangements for payment can be made and the patient has the appropriate knowledge to determine if the elective procedure should be scheduled.

3. PLACE

Place is also referred to as *distribution*, or how the product is delivered to the consumer. The physical location of the facility, hours of operation, type of facility (hospital, clinic, urgent care center, rehabilitation center, nursing home, etc.), and newer healthcare delivery models such as medical websites, smartphones, and house calls all factor into the consumer's assessment of place.

The competitive landscape has certainly changed the place component for traditional healthcare delivery. Chapter 3 will discuss the complex issues involved with the evolving competitive landscape in healthcare.

4. PROMOTION

Promotion involves any communication with consumers about the product offered. The prevalence of social media today increases the importance of Word of Mouth (WOM) communications by consumers. Online reviews such as Yelp, Healthgrades, RateMDs, Vitals, and ZocDoc and social media platforms such as Facebook, Twitter, and Instagram offer consumers immediate access to customer opinions about healthcare providers and healthcare organizations. Positive WOM works as a referral for consumers who place more importance on feedback from family and friends than from organized marketing activities by organizations. Social media usage with negative WOM requires organizations to continually monitor customer feedback to help improve service recovery (converting dissatisfied customers to satisfied customers).

Marketing promotions include advertising (television, radio, billboards, print media, social media), public relations and publicity (sponsorship of events, news stories), professional selling (typically used with sales of medical equipment and pharmaceuticals), and sales promotion (contests, coupons, loyalty programs, other incentives—although sales promotion is not used as often in healthcare organizations, it is often used in specialty practices such as dermatology and cosmetic procedures).

5. PHYSICAL EVIDENCE (PACKAGING)

Physical Evidence includes the packaging of healthcare products (equipment and pharmaceuticals) and the *servicescape* (ambience and physical environment) in which the healthcare service is delivered. It includes all of the physical evidence—buildings, logos, uniforms, equipment, etc. Imagine in your mind the aesthetic differences among the following hospital types: private hospital, concierge hospital, children's hospital, county hospital, and a VA hospital. Each hospital will look and feel very different to the consumer. For example, many hospitals differentiate their obstetrics departments by offering patients private rooms, in-room labor and delivery, aesthetically pleasing room décor, and comfortable newborn clothing.

6. PROCESS

Process is how the healthcare service is delivered to the patient. This includes everything the patient must do to receive the needed healthcare, from the first telephone call to set up an appointment to the final hospital discharge and post-operative care instructions.

The University of Texas MD Anderson Cancer Center in Houston, Texas, is an example of a hospital that differentiates itself from competitors through its processes. Patients and their families are met at the hospital with valet parking and individual pagers that notify patients when it is time for their appointment (radiology, laboratory, physician visit). Patients are also provided a free mobile application for patients, caregivers, and visitors that makes it easy to access information about scheduled appointments, messages, test results, medications, and other medical records. The patient-friendly processes complement the state-of-the-art medical care that is provided, but oftentimes, the process is more memorable to patients and determines whether a hospital experience is favorable or unfavorable for the patients and/or their families.

7. PEOPLE

Healthcare is a service delivered by **people** for people. Patients evaluate healthcare not only based on the quality and outcome of medical treatments, but also on how they perceive they were treated and the quality of interaction delivered by their healthcare provider. The quality of the service delivery will depend upon the skills, training, experience, and attitude of the person providing the service, which can vary significantly from one provider to the next. The very nature of healthcare service delivery means that the consumer is

Figure 1.3 Physician Circle of Struggle

also involved throughout the service experience, and each person's perception of the service that was delivered may vary from patient to patient and caregiver to caregiver.

Today more than ever, healthcare providers are managing the stress of high patient-to-provider ratios, controlling the high costs of healthcare services, focusing on quality patient outcomes, and managing the "business side" of healthcare. Administrators should strive to engage all of the employees within the healthcare organization who impact the patient's perception of the quality so that the patient always receives a positive and memorable experience. This will be discussed in greater detail in chapters 6 and 7.

TARGET MARKETS

The target market for any organization is the group of consumers most likely to use the organization's services or those consumers the organization desires to attract. Market segmentation is the process of dividing up the market into homogenous groups of consumers so that the marketing mix can be customized to meet the wants and needs of that particular market segment. There are many ways to segment markets, but the most common for healthcare are:

Figure 1.4 Market Segmentation

- Demographic—age, gender, race, ethnicity, income
- Geographic—where they live: state, region, country
- Psychographic—how they live: their attitudes, interests, and opinions
- Behavioral—how they will use your product or services (i.e., Botox injections for cosmetics, migraines, or hyperhidrosis)

VALUE PROPOSITION

One of the most important aspects of creating value for patients is the determination of the value proposition. A value proposition is a statement by the organization that provides a rationale for why consumers should purchase products (or services) from that organization and how its specific products better meet their wants and needs than other competitors with similar product offerings. Chapter 5 focuses on how healthcare organizations can create more value in the patient experience.

READING SELECTION

READING 1.1

MARKETING FOR DOCTORS AND STAFF

BY DREW STEVENS

Marketing is not about brochures and other collateral materials. Marketing is a state of consciousness in which the doctor and the practice create relationships. Physicians and staff are all marketing professionals. They must all operate to create relationships with patients. Marketing concentrates on relationships, and the manifestation of these relationships equates to brand equity. As patients learn about the practice and learn to appreciate the personnel and the culture they consistently return to them. The repetitive visits help to build the brand while lowering the cost of acquisition. This is vital to the practice because patients invest in relationships with those they know and those they trust.

Brands are instantly recognized and identified. Several national and regional surveys have shown that people (patients) choose a brand not because of price but simply for its name alone! People will make a purchase and choose a vendor solely for the brand. When I have a cold, I reach for a Kleenex, when I dine out, I request a Coke, and when I need a copy, I seek a Xerox. And, similar to these examples there are some brands that have become part of the pop culture. Imagine picking up the phone one morning and having a patient call you for an appointment because they were asked to do so! That is the power of a brand name.

There was a time when people would say "We are the Cadillac of the...." Cadillac had a cache that all desired. Today people say we are the Mercedes of the business. You would not hear many people say, "We are the Taurus of the business." If they did, they would be full of bull! Over the years Cadillac lost its reputation to other brands such as Jaguar, Mercedes, and so on. People believe they get what they pay for.

The value of a brand is that people will purchase for the brand's own sake and not after much market research and discretion. Mary Kay Cosmetics gives Cadillacs to top selling representatives with a purpose. I was in Dallas to receive one in 2005. I will never forget the faces, the aggressiveness, and the desire of those attendees waiting to receive their Cadillac! The allure of the Cadillac indicates its brand value in the Mary Kay consultant's eyes. Additionally, brands make products or services very attractive, and that attraction is often so strong that normal discrimination, skepticism, and price sensitivity are subordinated. A great example is Coca Cola. Without its original contents (cocaine) and without selling a can, Coca Cola is worth over $80 billion. They are the top selling brand in the world. Brands by their nature help to reduce perceived risk. When brands are strong, their very presence symbolizes a psychological reward.

Finally, your ability to build a brand confers a host of blessings such as patient loyalty, price inelasticity, and long-term profits. A loyal patient is nine times more profitable than a disloyal one. Further, an existing patient who is affected by your brand value helps to obtain new patients for you more efficiently, through referral, than a new one. Building a brand does not happen without expense and without time being spent on its acquisition. Research shows that it costs 200 to 400 times more to build brand equity but the long-term effects are worth it. Therefore it is imperative to implement branding as part of the practice's strategic focus.

TABLE 1.1 TOP 100 BRANDS

RANK	BRAND	SIZE
1	Coca Cola	68.7
2	IBM	60.0
3	Microsoft	56.6
4	GE	47.7
5	Nokia	34.8
6	McDonald's	32.2
7	Google	31.9
8	Toyota	31.3
9	Intel	30.6
10	Disney	28.4

Source: Interbrand 2009 Survey http://www.interbrand.com/best_global_brands.aspx

PERCEPTION IN BRANDING

There might well be a better computer manufacturer than Dell and there are probably better food chains than McDonald's. There are even better gymnasiums than Gold's. That is not important, what is important is the perception of the patient. Brands are fickle because perception is fickle.

Branding happens by default! Therefore, it is imperative to create the brand that promises you will provide to the maximum possible benefit. Tiffany's happened by default. Their brand states you get the blue box if you purchase for a certain amount. The brand is so strong patients do not care so much about the purchase as they do about standing in line to obtain the valuable Blue Box.

Perceived value crystallizes branding. The price is not considered when perception is high. Here are some examples of how branding helps in patient acquisition. With Volvo, people purchase safety, with Levis, comfort and style, with Gucci, style and luxury. Perception stems from the ability of the individuals to link their needs with value. Additionally, what promotes perception is emotion. People do not make rational decisions; they are emotional. Perception moves people. Perception creates action.

The following is a list of myths about marketing that requires clarification for branding.

- First, sales is not marketing and marketing is not selling. These terms are often confused. Marketing is about capturing the customer and offering value. Selling is exchange of value for money.
- Second, people make rational decisions. There is a maxim from one of my mentors who states, "Logic makes them think, Emotion makes them act!" (Weiss 2000). Purchases are made from emotional reactions. The excuse of logic is no longer relevant in a world where prospective customers are confronted with clutter.
- Third, marketing must rely on features and benefits. Folks, those days have left us for now. People buy value not features and benefits. Value stems from customer relationships and meeting the needs of customers.
- Fourth, changing advertising assists marketing and sales efforts. Not necessarily true. The relationship is enhanced by value. However, there is an issue with the number of times contact must be made with a customer—nine. With the receipt of over 8,500 messages per day there is too much clutter and it is vital that different ways are used to ensure brand visibility.

For you to begin to build a brand you must have several items in your marketing toolkit. However, when building a brand, it is vital that your focus is outward. Your intention is to show how you improve the condition of your patient. What are the results a patient gains in coming to you? Once your focus is on results you also need to consider the following points.

- Market: Does a need exist for the service or product that you offer? There are instances when a marketer can create a market but this is more difficult. It is vital then to understand how your service niches itself in the market. For example, with its flair for mobility, Apple continues to manifest its brand.
- Expertise: It is incumbent upon you to foster the skills and abilities necessary to deliver to the market. These skills must match the needs of the patients. Examples include logistics firms and distribution companies such as Amazon who are clearly unmatched in competitiveness.
- Passion: You must love what you do. Branding requires you to believe and act as if you're the best alternative. United Parcel Service constantly brags about what brown can do.
- Differentiation: So as not to be seen as similar to an array of alternatives, what do you deliver and provide to prove that you are drastically different from the rest? Is your message repeatable by others? For example, Ford, quality is the first point of emphasis or the former Avis ads that recommended itself because they "try harder."
- Testimonials: Do patients speak about you? When patients tell others of your strength, marketing collateral is unnecessary. How do others view you and what do they say?

When you begin to build a brand you will notice immediate changes in your business. A good brand will assist you in obtaining new patients. Prospective patients will be attracted to you. Your current patients will also want to remain with you. Your image and value will remain and patients will ignore noisy interruptions from competitors based on your value. Finally, you will comprehend what you do and create better dialogue with others interested in your services. Your articulation works like a global positioning system and guides you to better opportunities in less time.

DEVELOPING A MINDSET FOR MARKETING

If you are like most doctors, then you will certainly have three big fears: death, taxes, and public speaking. However, I would like to add one more: marketing. Most doctors do not think about it, do not like to do it, and would rather have someone else take care of this crucial responsibility. Yet, if doctors are not keen on building business, then there will be no person to treat. Ah yes, a Catch 22 situation. This is like saying, which is more important, the chicken or the egg?

With this in mind, doctors must have a marketing mindset. Yes, your mindset must change from where you are today and shift toward business development. Admittedly, this is no easy task but it is imperative to make the shift so that your practice progresses from merely surviving to thriving.

Think of it this way. Marketing is always present everywhere. From the moment you awake until the moment you fall asleep you are immersed in marketing. You watch the news, open a box of Granola, brush your teeth, and get dressed. In that minimal time you are introduced to products and services that can be delivered to you or can be purchased by you because of marketing and its related activities. Marketing is required to bring valuable products and services to you. After all, marketing is required for the acquisition and retention of customers like you. Further, marketing helps to provide you the products and services you want as well as need.

None of these can happen unless you have a marketing mindset. What is a marketing mindset? As mentioned earlier in the chapter, marketing is an exchange of information that helps to establish relationships so that customers (patients) understand value. Value in the marketing world especially for medical professionals is the relationship and trust built around the benefits of care provided and the sacrifice(s) necessary for the patient to receive these benefits. Value is not about quality, priority, or anything else other than a set of philosophical and psychological inferences that create the processes of practice resulting in patient satisfaction. And, to establish the processes, marketing uses a series of activities to institutionalize this philosophical attitude into the practice. Therefore, marketing requires a new mindset or quality, providing value, information, communication, feedback, idea exchange, and most importantly patient service.

A key aspect of the marketing mindset is to build relationships. Realistically we can say that you are in the medical profession but, pragmatically to grow a thriving practice, you are actually in the business of building relationships. To help nurture and grow your practice you should get involved on a daily basis with activities that take you further into your local community so that your practice grows. More important than advertising, the key to establishing a practice based on value is relationship.

Doctors, who are above average, will differentiate themselves by creating relationships so as to build rapport with the patient. For example one might argue that consulting a doctor is a commodity business much like buying eggs at a local grocer or obtaining a haircut at a local barber. However, there is a reason why customers shop in specific places—relationship. We can argue that there are some services such as laser, acupuncture, and so on that aid a practice because of their distinctive products and services. We might even argue that certain physicians can differentiate themselves based on price but the marketing mindset requires more of an intangible than tangible benefit. Patients align products and services with a fee, therefore the value they associate is the exchange of the fee for the value (benefit) received. Incidentally, this is the definition of selling, something discussed a bit later in this chapter. But suffice it to say that the fee is related to the tangible gain. Therefore, these are commodities and they pay a fee.

The doctor who is into relationships and creates a marketing mindset is different. The best patients do not associate a relationship and trust with a fee; their value is incalculable. Relationships then have intrinsic value and no amount of money can be equated to the trust and respect inspired by the doctor, and prospective patients would not dare place a fee on them. These relationships then last lifelong, downplaying barriers of resistance while also creating more awareness of and brand for the doctor.

PLACING DISTINCTION IN YOUR MARKETING MINDSET

To help you foster relationships, understand that personality and behavior must also be part of your overall functioning. For example, I can take two different doctors and place them in the same medical professionals program. They attend the same classes, get the same grades, and even get the same grade in the exam. However, their relationships with patients will be different depending on their innate skills.

There is nothing better for growing a profitable practice than trusting patients who want and need your services. They believe in their heart that you will get them out of immediate pain and ensure that it does not return. This trust is something not easily achieved by others and this relationship must be guarded like the Hope Diamond or Crown Jewels. Arguing with patients, treating them poorly, not returning calls—any of these things can sour a relationship that takes years to build. Creating a mindset is not only worth it, it is a must for your practice. When you develop a mindset of value, of relationship, and of desire, you build a wealth of opportunities both for the present and the future.

There are many who will that suggest relationship building is based on foremost in the mind for doctors who seek to build trusting and long-lasting relationships with their patients.

1. The Law of Value: Value has long been discussed in the marketing and business development world. With many doctors to choose from, patients seek value so as to mitigate time and expense in getting proper help. Value is the benefit that patients receive as a result of the trust and respect for service that they develop. In today's competitive market, value provides intrinsic fees for services as well as the differentiation of services. When doctors build value-based relationships, they have a strong defense against competition.

2. The Law of Constant Contact: Social Media and software known as Customer Relationship Management (CRM) allow a multitude of ways to constantly remain in contact with present and former patients. Although trite, "out of sight" *is* "out of mind." There is too much competition and the Internet makes it too easy to find another doctor or another way to ease back pain or stiffness. When you remain in constant contact you can not only be differentiated from the doctor down the street, but also be remembered immediately when patients require your services.

3. The Law of Testimonials and Case Study: While this chapter is meant to help you with your business development there are times when contrary methods work better than conventional ones. Many physicians develop websites, blogs, Facebook pages, and so on telling stories and facts related to medical professional care. Prospective patients desire to hear more about your brand of care. With that in mind, it is best to collect and integrate into your marketing as many testimonials and case studies as possible. This implies that you must have former patients boasting of your efforts in their cases to new patients who desire to know how you can help them. Additionally, patients actually want to hear from others because the word of mouth (WOM) marketing helps to break down barriers and build higher levels of trust and respect.

4. The Law of Short-Term Transactions: If you are like many, your phone rings incessantly from cold callers who want to sell you goods that you have little

need for. Not only are these calls intrusive, but they are also transactional. Each person on the call is only interested in one thing—getting you to say yes to something before the end of the call. Physicians cannot perform in this manner. Each interaction from meeting at a networking event to perhaps the Report of Findings helps build the trust factor. Each discussion helps to continue the discussion, which develops the relationship that influences the business aspect. The more doctors think of continuing relationships the better for longer-term success of the practice.

5. The Law of Availability: The medical profession is a service-based business, and most business in the United States is service-based. Yet how many times have you, as a patient, made calls, left voice mails, and sent emails all to be ignored, forgotten, or downplayed by your recipient. There are too many physicians or their staff who conduct business in this fashion. One can never cease to wonder at the different ways in which patients are often ignored. Therefore, be "patient-service" savvy. Ensure that all aspects of your practice engage in this important art to help you retain your most vital asset.

6. The Law of Community: As you might have noticed during the Marketing Acceleration© discussion, building a community is a large factor in creating value for patients. When others in the community know you better, they understand your practice, your methods, and your values and want to know you even better. The only way to ensure that others know your value is to get into the community and show it. Some of the best ways to do that is to get involved in local community activities such as religious, athletic, and civic events. Many of these take very little time and money and will make you the "Vicar of Value" because of the awareness such volunteerism brings. You might make contributions, sponsor a local event, or even offer to mail envelopes or lick stamps. No matter what your involvement, large or small, your stewardship will be rewarding.

7. The Law of Recommended Resources: Physicians need not always be a dictionary of answers. Being a valuable resource for additional health and wellness information will make you more valued by your patients. They will honor the information you provide and appreciate your concern for their welfare. This alone will make you a valuable asset.

REFERENCE

Gallo, C. July 21, 2012. "7 Sure-Fire Ways Apple Store Converts Browsers into Buyers." *Forbes.* http://www.forbes.com/sites/carminegallo/2012/07/25/7-sure-fire-ways-apple-store-converts-browsers-into-buyers/ (accessed July 12, 2015).

REFLECTIONS ON THE READING SELECTION

We offer the following editorial commentary on the reading selection.

1. On p. 13, most likely the author meant to state "customers" rather than "patients" because it would not be appropriate to use "patients" when referring to Tiffany's. The relevant point is that branding can help your organization differentiate from competitors with something as simple as unique packaging.

2. In the section on branding, the discussion about market, expertise, passion, differentiation, and testimonials can also be helpful in determining your value proposition. Always try to look through the eyes of your patients and prospective patients to "see what they see" regarding your organization.

3. With regard to Developing a Mindset for Marketing, the author refers to "doctors," but this mindset also applies to all healthcare providers. By their innate desire to help others and their previous medical training and experience, healthcare providers have previously only focused on delivering quality care to their patients. The very idea of the "business" of healthcare runs counter to how healthcare providers want to think of healthcare delivery. We never suggest that quality care should be compromised for the sake of a business decision, but healthcare administrators must learn to manage the organization effectively and efficiently to maximize the capabilities and long-term financial stability of the organization. We understand that this business mindset is a paradigm shift that can be difficult for healthcare providers to embrace.

4. In the second-to-last paragraph of Developing a Mindset for Marketing, the reading selection author states "a bit later in this chapter." This reading selection is only an excerpt and does not contain the entire chapter.

5. In the 7 Laws of Relationship in Marketing, we suggest a phrase that is similar to the "out of sight" and "out of mind" concepts is "top of mind awareness." If a patient needs an urgent care center, you want them to immediately think of *your* urgent care center, and not your competitors. The same is true for specialists, including orthopedists, pulmonologists, and gastroenterologists, and ancillary services such as home health agencies. When patients or family members are faced with finding new healthcare providers, oftentimes top of mind awareness is a determining factor in the selection process. This is also the case with referring providers. When patients ask for referrals from either the healthcare provider or support staff, those providers and/or organizations that come to mind are then recommended to the patient. If your healthcare organization relies on referrals from healthcare providers, you should also include business-to-business marketing efforts in your marketing plan to increase the top of mind awareness for your organization rather than using only business-to-consumer marketing efforts.

6. We agree testimonials are an effective means to share your patients' stories to help build trust and reinforce your brand. However, due to HIPAA requirements, always obtain written permission by your patients to use their testimonials. To protect their privacy, avoid using protected health information (PHI), and we recommend only using the patient's first name. We also recommend if you have a legal department in your organization that it be contacted to review any patient testimonial prior to public release.

7. In The Law of Community section, the reading selection author mentions Marketing Acceleration© discussion. This reading selection is only an excerpt and does not contain the entire chapter.

APPLICATION AND SYNTHESIS

"I realized that as a doctor you're just a guest in your patient's life… I shifted from asking the question 'Am I being a good host?' to the magic question 'Am I being a good guest?'… I strive to be a good guest in people's lives." —*Kaveh Safavi, MD, JD, managing director for Accenture's Global Health Practice* (Accenture.com, 2016)

QUESTIONS FOR DISCUSSION

1. What did the term "marketing" mean to you before you read this chapter? Did your perception change after reading the chapter? If yes, how?

2. What is the role of marketing in your healthcare organization?

3. For your organization, answer the following questions:

   a. Who is your target market?

   b. What is your value proposition?

   c. Which P of the 7Ps is the most critical for your target market?

4. In the 7Ps for Creating Value model, what is the greatest challenge to implement for your healthcare organization? Why do you think it is difficult?

5. How do you shift the paradigm in your organization from being a good host to being a good guest as Dr. Kaveh Safavi suggests?

SUMMARY OF MAIN POINTS

After reading this chapter, you should be able to:

√ Distinguish among the 7Ps of the marketing mix (p. 5–9)
√ Identify the target market and determine the various ways to segment markets (p. 9)
√ Create a value proposition (p. 10)
√ Understand how branding impacts patient acquisition (p. 11–16)
√ Identify the 7 Laws of Relationship in Marketing (p. 17–18)

COMPREHENSION ASSESSMENT

1. Why is the 7Ps model more appropriate for healthcare organizations than the traditional 4Ps?

2. Why is it important for organizations to identify their target market?

3. What are the differences between demographic, geographic, psychographic, and behavioral market segmentation?

4. Why should organizations create a value proposition?

5. Explain why branding is important for healthcare organizations.

6. Discuss the importance of relationships in healthcare marketing.

CONCLUSION

This chapter provided you with an overview of marketing—specifically, marketing in healthcare organizations. You learned about target marketing and market segmentation so that your marketing efforts can be directed more appropriately and efficiently. You should also have a better understanding of how patients may view your organization through the lens of a marketing mindset. You understand how you can better position your organization through a well-defined value proposition. Finally, we discussed the importance of branding and how relationships can enhance the overall perception patients develop about you and your organization.

Now that you better understand the principles of marketing, the next chapter will focus on the changing healthcare paradigm shift and what these changes mean to you and your healthcare organization.

REFERENCES

American Marketing Association (2015). Retrieved from https://www.ama.org/AboutAMA/Pages/Definition-of-Marketing.aspx.

Accenture (2016). *Perspectives: Getting your money's worth in the health industry*. Retrieved from https://www.accenture.com/us-en/insight-perspectives-health-q-and-a-kaveh-safavi.

IMAGE CREDITS

- Fig. 1.0: Copyright © Depositphotos/Wavebreakmedia.
- Fig. 1.3: Copyright © Depositphotos/Wavebreakmedia.
- Fig. 1.4: Copyright © Depositphotos/dizanna.

2
CHAPTER

THE HEALTHCARE PARADIGM SHIFT

hospitals

senate

medica

uphold

LEARNING OBJECTIVES

In this chapter, you will learn about the following:

- Changes in the healthcare paradigm shift
- Topics reported in the Hospital Consumer Assessment of Healthcare Providers and Systems (HCAHPS)
- Impact of technology on healthcare

HEALTH CARE REFORM

obamacare

politicians · business · campaign

debates · president · costs · congress · debt · democrats · taxes

doctors · dependents · issues

agents · insurance

brokers

republicans

false or true facts

INTRODUCTION

As stated by Camp et al. (2017), "Healthcare is arguably the single most important service experience because it impacts one's quality of life and physical well-being." Healthcare in the United States continues to be one of the most discussed political issues of our time. The evolution of healthcare due to governmental mandates shifted dramatically when the Patient Protection and Affordable Care Act, also known as the Affordable Care Act (ACA) and Obamacare, was signed into law in 2010 (Department of Health & Human Services, 2015). With the inauguration of President Donald J. Trump in January 2017, healthcare continues to change, which results in an increased level of uncertainty that comes with change, thus making the healthcare paradigm shift even more dramatic. A **paradigm shift** occurs when the way of thinking or of doing something is replaced by a different thought or method.

The new governmental mandates create a shift from the traditional volume-based model of reimbursement to a newer, value-based reimbursement model. Even if the ACA is completely repealed, it is likely that transparency in pricing and quality will continue to impact patient decision-making with regard to hospitals, clinics, and providers. The Center for Medicare & Medicaid Services (CMS) historically drives most reimbursement models for healthcare services in that commercial insurance providers and Medicaid often base their reimbursement scales on a set percentage of Medicare fees. For the most current guidelines, www.medicare.gov is the official government website that serves as the best source for updated information.

NOTES FROM PRACTICE

Figure 2.1 Paula E. Anthony

As for my own education, I have a BA from Wesleyan University, an MBA from Case Western Reserve University, and a PhD from the University of Texas at Tyler. For the past 20 years, I have been privileged to serve as the vice president and chief information officer for ETMC Regional Healthcare System in Tyler, Texas. This, my dream job, has allowed me to work with professionals across the entire healthcare continuum, finding and implementing technology solutions that advance the delivery of exceptional patient care. I was also recently appointed to the Texas Health Services Authority Board of Directors by Governor Greg Abbott in the hopes that I might contribute to the state's plans to improve the sharing of clinical information among healthcare providers.

Prior to joining ETMC, I spent 10 years with Ernst & Young and was responsible for the firm's Southwest Health Care Information Technology practice—another incredible job in which I worked with countless healthcare providers in working through their IT-related challenges. But I got my start in healthcare working for a small IT vendor that sold exclusively into hospital C-suites. This company offered me one of my first and most important life lessons: If you can speak and write well and think creatively, the rest can be taught.

PATIENT EXPERIENCES AND REIMBURSEMENT

Now more than ever before, the focus in healthcare is not only about providing high-quality medical care, but even more attention is placed upon the patient's *perception* of the quality of their healthcare experience. It is important for healthcare providers to understand how patient expectations impact satisfaction and, ultimately, their determination of quality. This is particularly relevant due to the current CMS rules that tie the patient's assessment of their experience to the actual reimbursement received by providers.

"Frankly, you are so far sighted that you can see the future of healthcare."

Figure 2.2 Future of Healthcare

SURVEY OF PATIENTS' EXPERIENCES

Expectations include how the patient perceives they will be treated and whether or not the outcome of that treatment met, exceeded, or fell short of the patient's perceptions prior to the service experience. Many patients now expect to receive a service similar to what they would receive by retailers, particularly in specialty areas such as obstetrics, cosmetic surgery, pediatrics, radiology (mammography), and other elective procedures. Amazon has had a major impact on retailing; so have consumer expectations in general. Consumers now have a 24/7 mindset. They expect extended hours and availability of assistance on their own time schedule. "One size fits all" no longer applies because consumers demand customization of their experiences. Perhaps the most challenging aspect is that they demand what they want now, not later. These changes can be summed up as immediacy, choice, and personalization.

Satisfaction is a measure of a consumer's determination of what is received based on what is expected. If they received what they expected, or more than they expected,

Figure 2.3 Satisfaction Pain Meter

they are satisfied. If they received less than they expected, they are dissatisfied. Satisfaction is based on a patient's perceptions, not necessarily the actual quality of care they received. This can be the most difficult concept for healthcare providers to understand and accept because providers may believe that if the patient has a good medical outcome, they should believe that they have received quality healthcare. However, patient satisfaction is not only based on the actual medical outcome, but on the entire experience as a whole. This often includes the opinions of family members and friends based on how they were treated and/or involved in the healthcare process. It is hard to comprehend that a patient may be more satisfied with a less than optimal outcome as opposed to an optimal outcome, but this may depend more on *how* they experienced the healthcare process in its entirety.

The CMS requires that hospitals survey their patients to rate their experiences with their inpatient stay. HCAHPS is a national, standardized survey that collects data on patients' evaluations of hospital care. HCAHPS are administered through approved third-party vendors who collect and administer the surveys on behalf of their hospital clients. These ratings provide consumers with information that can be used to objectively make comparisons between hospitals on a local and national level. The survey asks discharged patients a series of 27 questions about the hospital experience. It is distributed to a random sample of patients 48 hours to six weeks after their hospital discharge. The ratings are publicly reported and could, therefore, ultimately impact the hospital's overall reputation within its local community and the brand equity of the organization.

One interesting aspect of HCAHPS is that the survey questions do not specifically measure satisfaction (Camp et al., 2017). For more information and frequently asked questions, this is a useful website: https://www.cms.gov/Medicare/Quality-Initiatives-Patient-Assessment-Instruments/HospitalQualityInits/Downloads/

HospitalHCAHPSFactSheet201007.pdf. Beginning in 2016, outpatient and ambulatory surgery centers began collecting similar patient satisfaction data through the Outpatient and Ambulatory Surgery Center Consumer Assessment of Healthcare Providers and Systems (OAS CAHPS) survey, but participation by these organizations is optional. HCAHPS is discussed in greater detail in the reading in this chapter.

Another struggle that hospital administrators must manage is one of the unique aspects involved with the hospital experience—multiple touchpoints exist throughout the patient's hospital stay. For example, front desk personnel, nurses, phlebotomists, radiological technicians, physician assistants, hospitalists, and other hospital personnel are in patient-facing roles, which means that they come into direct contact with the patient during their hospital stay. This makes the determination of a quality experience for the patient a more complex decision. Thus, it becomes even more difficult for management to accurately determine how to improve patient experience scores. Increasing value for the patient will be covered in chapters 5, 6, and 7.

HOSPITAL VALUE-BASED PURCHASING PROGRAM

HCAHPS results represent 25% of the value-based purchasing score, which is calculated as part of the hospital's Medicare reimbursement payments. The hospital value-based purchasing program is one of the ACA's programs to change the emphasis from quantity to quality. It is unclear whether the value-based purchasing program will continue if the ACA is repealed.

TECHNOLOGY IN HEALTHCARE

The Food and Drug Administration (2017) identifies digital health as "categories such as mobile health (mHealth), health information technology (IT), wearable devices, telehealth and telemedicine, and personalized medicine." The advances in technology for medical devices create the ability to better communicate to other providers and healthcare systems. Because of this, digital health offers providers and other stakeholders many advantages, including the ability to reduce inefficiencies (i.e., medical tests/procedures duplication, drug interactions, etc.), improved access to healthcare, cost reductions, quality improvements, and a more customized approach to solving healthcare problems for patients. Technology also attempts to make the patient experience more user-friendly by engaging patients directly in their treatment experience through online mechanisms such as patient portals that allow patients to view, download, and transmit their health information more easily, as mandated by the American Recovery and Reinvestment Act of 2009 (Blumenthal, 2011).

Figure 2.4 Healthcare is Mobile

READING SELECTION

READING 2.1

FISCAL YEAR (FY) 2016 RESULTS FOR THE CMS HOSPITAL VALUE-BASED PURCHASING PROGRAM

HOSPITAL VALUE-BASED PURCHASING (VBP) PROGRAM OVERVIEW

The Hospital Value-Based Purchasing (VBP) Program adjusts what CMS pays hospitals under the Inpatient Prospective Payment System (IPPS) based on the quality of care they give patients. For FY 2016, the law requires that the applicable percent reduction, the portion of Medicare payments available to fund the program's value-based incentive payments, go up from 1.50 to 1.75 percent of the base operating Medicare Severity diagnosis-related group (MS-DRG) payment amounts to all participating hospitals. We estimate that the total amount available for value-based incentive payments in FY 2016 will be approximately $1.5 billion.

The Hospital VBP Program is one of many Affordable Care Act programs Medicare is putting into place to pay for quality instead of quantity. For FY 2016, it gives a snapshot of how hospitals are performing on several important patient care domains.

The Hospital VBP Program is part of our long-standing effort to structure Medicare payments to improve healthcare quality, including hospital inpatient care. This is the fourth year of value-based purchasing for the largest share of Medicare spending, affecting payment for inpatient stays in over 3,000 hospitals across the country. We now pay hospitals for inpatient acute care services based on the *quality of* care, not just the *quantity of* services provided.

We've been increasing the program's number of quality domains and measures used to evaluate performance. Our goal is to include a broader, richer set of measures over time and aligning with the National Quality Strategy (NQS).

The quality domains for FY 2016 were:

- 10 percent: Clinical process of care
- 25 percent: Patient experience of care (HCAHPS survey)
- 40 percent: Outcome (hospital mortality measures for acute myocardial infarction, heart failure, and pneumonia, the central line-associated bloodstream infection measure, the catheter associated urinary tract infection measure, the surgical site infection strata, and the AHRQ PSI-90 Composite)
- 25 percent: Efficiency (Medicare Spending per Beneficiary measure)

We believe the program will result in improved patient outcomes, safety, and patients' care experience.

FISCAL YEAR 2016 VBP PROGRAM RESULTS

We have posted the Hospital VBP incentive payment adjustment factors for FY 2016 at https://www.cms.gov/Medicare/Medicare-Fee-for-Service-Payment/AcutelnpatientPPS/FY2016-IPPS-Final-Rule-Home-Page-Items/FY2016-IPPS-Final-Rule-Tables.html.

We'll pay most hospitals more or less for each Medicare fee-for-service discharge in FY 2016 than they would've been paid in the absence of the program. Hospitals' payments will depend on:

- How well they measured up to their peers on important healthcare quality measures during a performance period
- How much they have improved over time

We will not include those hospitals excluded from the Hospital VBP Program in FY 2016 in the payment adjustment factors table. Hospitals excluded from the Hospital Value-Based Purchasing Program do not incur the reduction of 1.75 percent and are not eligible to receive other incentives.

Hospitals around the country are tracking their performance on Hospital VBP measures because they want to give better care. They use external performance dashboards to continuously monitor the care they give and their incentive payment adjustment. Hospitals' focus on giving better care should benefit patients.

For FY 2016, more hospitals will have a positive change in their base operating MS-DRG payments than will have a negative change. In total, over 1,800 hospitals will have a positive payment adjustment which will provide increases to approximately 600 more hospitals in comparison to reductions in the fiscal year.

In FY 2016, about half of hospitals will see a small change in their base operating MS-DRG payments (between −0.4 and 0.4 percent). The highest performing hospital in FY 2016 will receive a net change in payments of slightly more than 3 percent after 1.75 percent is withheld. The worst performing hospital, receiving a Total Performance Score (TPS) of 0, will see the maximum reduction of 1.75 percent and will not receive an incentive payment.

COMPUTING THE VBP SCORE

The Hospital VBP Program is funded each year from a reduction of participating hospitals' base operating MS-DRG payments for the applicable fiscal year. These payment reductions are redistributed to hospitals as incentive payments, based on their TPS as required by the statute. The actual amount earned by each hospital will depend on:

- Its TPS.
- Its value-based incentive payment percentage.
- On the total amount available for value-based incentive payments.

Hospitals may earn back a value-based incentive payment percentage that is less than, equal to, or more than the applicable percent reduction for that program year. This means hospitals could see an increase, a decrease, or no change to its Medicare IPPS payments for the applicable fiscal year.

The estimated amount of base operating MS-DRG payment amount reductions for FY 2016 and the amount available for value-based incentive payments for FY 2016 discharges is about $1.5 billion.

In FY 2016, hospitals' total performance scores were based on four domains:

- Clinical process of care.
- Patient experience of care.
- Outcome.
- Efficiency.

Hospitals' TPS's were subject to minimum case and measure requirements. Also, they had to have a domain score for at least two of the four domains in order to have a TPS calculated. Hospitals that do not meet the minimum requirements do not have their payments adjusted in the corresponding fiscal year. For every measure, each of the hospitals participating in the Hospital VBP Program receives an improvement score or achievement score, whichever is higher.

CMS adopted the following policies that will modify the FY 2017 Hospital VBP Program:

- Addition of two new Safety measures;
- Addition of one new Clinical Care—Process measure;
- Re-adoption of the current version of the CLABSI measure; and
- Removal of six "topped-out" clinical process measures.

Over 78 percent of the measures in the Hospital VBP Program will assess health outcomes, patient experience, and cost.

We will adopt two new outcome measures for the new Safety domain:

- Hospital-onset methicillin-resistant Staphylococcus aureus (MRSA) bacteremia and Clostridium difficile infection.
- Clinical Care–Process measure: early elective deliveries (PC-01).

FY 2017 DOMAIN WEIGHTING

We have finalized new quality domains based on the NQS and domain weighting for FY 2017. Due to the large number of "topped out" measures that we are removing from the FY 2017 measure set, the finalized FY 2017 domain weighting for hospitals that receive a score on all domains reduces the weight of the Clinical Care–Process subdomain to 5 percent and increases the weight of the Safety domain to 20 percent.

We have finalized a policy to require hospitals to receive domain scores in at least three of the four domains in order to be eligible to receive a TPS and payment adjustments, a change from the policy requiring at least two of the four domains in FY 2015 and FY 2016.

FY 2018 MEASURES, DOMAINS, & WEIGHTING

The FY 2018 measure set adds a three-item Care Transition dimension to the Patient and Caregiver Centered Experience of Care/Care Coordination domain. We will normalize the scores in the domain to account for the new dimension. We have also removed the AMI-7a and IMM-2 measures from the Clinical Care–Process subdomain and will move the remaining PC-01 measure to the Safety domain. When we removed the AMI-7a and IMM-2 measures from the Hospital VBP Program and moved the PC-01 measure to the Safety domain, we finalized the proposal to remove the Clinical Care–Process subdomain entirely.

We have included four domains for the FY 2018 Hospital VBP Program:

- Clinical Care.
- Patient Experience and Caregiver Centered Experience/Care Coordination.
- Safety.
- Efficiency and Cost Reduction.

Each domain will be weighted at 25 percent of a hospital's TPS. We will continue to require hospitals to receive domain scores in at least three of the four domains in order to be eligible to receive TPS and payment adjustments.

FY 2019, 2020, 2021, & 2022 MEASURES

We have adopted one new hospital-level risk-standardized complication rate following elective hip and knee arthroplasty measure with:

- A 30-month performance period for FY 2019.
- A 36-month performance period for FY 2020.

We have also adopted one new hospital-level risk-standardized mortality measure monitoring mortality rates following Chronic Obstructive Pulmonary Disease (COPD) hospitalizations for FY 2021. Hospitals will be measured based on a 36-month performance period in FY 2021.

MOVING FORWARD

As we more closely link patient outcomes and treatment costs to value-based hospital payment, it's important to remember that the Hospital VBP program not only aims for quality gains on paper, it also aims to promote a culture focused on the needs of patients.

Value-based purchasing in Medicare continues to move ahead, improving healthcare for people with Medicare now and creating a healthcare system that will ensure quality care for generations to come.

ADDITIONAL INFORMATION

To see the FY 2016 value-based incentive payment adjustment factors, please visit: https://www.cms.gov/Medicare/Medicare-Fee-for-Service-Payment/AcutelnpatientPPS/FY2016-IPPS-Final-Rule-Home-Page-ltems/FY2016-IPPS-Final-Rule-Tables.html?DLPage=1&DLEntries=10&DLSort=0&DLSortDir=ascending.

REFLECTIONS ON THE READING SELECTION

We offer the following editorial commentary on the reading selection.

1. Governmental regulations can certainly change at any time, particularly due to political shifts such as the presidential election in 2016. At the time of this textbook's publication date, the Survey of Patients' Experiences and the Fiscal Year (FY) 2016 Results for the CMS Hospital Value-Based Purchasing Program readings are the most current resources for patient experiences and reimbursement guidelines. However, we understand that these are subject to change, so we strongly recommend that you refer to www.medicare.gov for the most current policies that are in place.

2. It is important to note that the Surveys of Patients' Experiences that are publicly available online at the Hospital Compare website (http://www.medicare.gov/hospitalcompare) are only aggregate numbers rather than individual survey responses. This makes it even more difficult for healthcare managers to fully understand the specific drivers of satisfaction with regard to the patient experience. However, we recommend that hospitals contact their vendor directly for item-level analyses, which would be more useful for strategic organizational decisions. The most current HCAHPS information can be found at http://www.hcahpsonline.org.

APPLICATION AND SYNTHESIS

"Patients spend more time outside the doctor's office than in it, and they have healthcare needs that arise outside of the office... If you can look up your lab results in the portal or e-mail me to ask about your medication, it saves you a phone call... If I can answer a question over e-mail, it may save you an office visit." — *Daniel Sands, MD, MPH, practicing physician at Beth Israel Deaconess Medical Center in Boston* (Accenture.com, 2016)

QUESTIONS FOR DISCUSSION

1. How do HCAHPS surveys impact the practice of medicine?

2. What do you believe is the impact of sending out a questionnaire 48 hours after care is received or six weeks after? If the time frame could be changed, what differences might occur with regard to patient responses? What would you recommend and why?

3. What are other digital tools healthcare organizations should consider that might impact marketing strategies?

SUMMARY OF MAIN POINTS

After reading this chapter, you should be able to:

√ Synthesize and apply changes in the healthcare paradigm to healthcare organizations (p. 25–26)
√ Identify what the HCAHPS survey measures and how it is administered (p. 27–29)
√ Discuss how digital health impacts healthcare delivery (p. 29–30)

COMPREHENSION ASSESSMENT

1. How has legislation impacted how organizations approach patient satisfaction?

2. What is the HCAHPS survey, and how is it used by Medicare?

3. What is the value-based modifier?

4. How is the HCAHPS survey administered?

5. What are some tools used by organizations in digital health?

CONCLUSION

In this chapter, we discussed the dramatic changes that have occurred in recent years in healthcare. This focus on how healthcare should be delivered continues to be a political "hot button;" thus, it is always subject to change. However, in an environment where transparency and consumer satisfaction remain at the forefront of consumer and governmental expectations, measuring and publicly reporting patient satisfaction and outcomes will most likely exist in the public domain for years to come. For these reasons, we believe it is important to understand HCAHPS and how it will continue to capture patients' experiences with healthcare providers and systems.

Hopefully, you have learned more about HCAHPS and how these patient surveys impact reimbursements for hospitals and consumer perceptions. The next chapter will focus on the competitive landscape within the healthcare industry and how this should impact an organization's marketing strategy.

REFERENCES

Accenture Consulting (2017). *Getting your money's worth in the health industry*. Retrieved from https://www.accenture.com/us-en/insight-perspectives-health-q-and-a-kaveh-safavi.

Blumenthal, D. (2011). Implementation of the federal health information technology initiative *The New England Journal of Medicine*, *365*(25), 2426–2431.

Camp, K. M., James, K., Babin, B., and Swimberghe, K. (2017). Hedonic and Utilitarian Value Drivers for Patient Satisfaction: Perceptual Differences between Patients and Providers. *The Journal of Applied Management and Entrepreneurship*, *22*(1), 6–27.

Consumer Reports (2013). *The doctor will e-mail you now: Five reasons patient portals can lead to better health.* Retrieved from http://www.consumerreports. org/cro/magazine/2014/01/the-doctor-will-email-you-now/index.htm.

Department of Health & Human Services (2015). *Key features of the Affordable Care Act by year.* Retrieved from: http://www.hhs.gov/healthcare/facts/timeline/ timeline-text.html.

Food & Drug Administration (2017). *Digital health.* Retrieved from: http://www.fda. gov/medicaldevices/digitalhealth/.

IMAGE CREDITS

3

CHAPTER

UNDERSTANDING THE COMPETITIVE ENVIRONMENT

LEARNING OBJECTIVES

In this chapter, you will learn about the following:

- Concierge medicine
- Changes in the healthcare marketplace
- Medical tourism
- Telemedicine
- Digital health tools

INTRODUCTION

The competitive environment within healthcare is more complex than ever before. Previously, the competitive landscape mostly consisted of nonprofit and for-profit hospitals, hospital-owned and physician-owned outpatient clinics, and urgent care centers. This has now been expanded to include retail clinics in discount stores and pharmacies, medical tourism, mobile medicine, concierge medicine (also known as boutique medicine or retainer-based medicine), and the dramatic increase in walk-in centers.

NOTES FROM PRACTICE

Figure 3.1 Felix Liu

Felix Liu earned his PhD in chemistry from Tulane University. He conducted research in the area of using nuclear magnetic resonance spectroscopy and computational chemistry to elucidate the structure-dynamics-function relationship of carbohydrates and proteins. Following his real interests, he changed his career in midlife and became a software engineer. He entered the healthcare information technology field as a data warehouse and business intelligence developer at the Ohio State University Medical Center. He worked on projects for clinical workflow improvement, quality reporting, and biomedical informatics. A few weeks after one of his applications was put into real use, a pathologist called him to say that in that day for one patient, his application made a clinical difference toward the correct diagnosis. "That was the pinnacle of my career as a developer!" he claimed.

Moving into management as a team manager, Liu led a group of informaticians to develop novel informatics tools in support of biomedical research. He became the associate director of research IT at the University of Florida Health, where he designed the software and workflow for the first clinical pharmacogenetics implementation in the nation.

Taking a new position with the CHRISTUS Trinity Mother Frances Health System as its inaugural director of analytics, he streamlined the reporting process, developed internal standards, implemented and promoted self-servicing business intelligence, and led the IT efforts in population health, patient care quality, and operational efficiency. The demand on business acumen prompted him to pursue his MBA degree in healthcare management. His department served a wide range of internal customers as well as external clients and government agencies.

In addition, to stay abreast of technological development, Liu paid extra attention to both the marketing of the departmental capabilities and customer service.

> "Many people think that serving internal customers [is] easier, because your customers won't run away. In reality, it requires more efforts in work ethics, service quality, customer care, and relationship building. Your customer base is fixed, and trying to do things right with your next customer is not an option."

CONCIERGE MEDICINE—CASE STUDY

CONCIERGE MEDICINE—A SERVICES PERSPECTIVE

BY KERRIE ANNE AMBORT-CLARK, MBA

INTRODUCTION

Concierge medicine is a growing practice embodied by a personalized patient-to-physician relationship through the delivery of healthcare services. Through

Figure 3.2 House Calls Have Changed

this model, patients most often retain their primary care physician or family physicians through memberships that are billed monthly or annually; fees are then paired with the doctors' services that are out of pocket or, in some cases, billed through patients' insurance providers.

Concierge physicians often practice with a lower physician-to-patient ratio than in a traditional family practice. This ratio allows physicians to be more readily available to their patients and therefore enables a customized model for delivering healthcare services. Access to concierge medicine allows patients to build a personable relationship with their physician while facilitating an "on-call" atmosphere for the enrollee's healthcare needs.

Dr. Drew is a family medicine doctor. Dr. Drew provides comprehensive concierge healthcare for individuals and their families in his community. Dr. Drew offers a variety of memberships for his patients so he can reach as much of his community as possible.

The *Membership Plans* consist of a Platinum, Gold, and Silver Plan. Dr. Drew does not take private insurance, and all services are direct billed to the patient. A price sheet of common services is provided annually to each enrollee, and prices may be subject to change with notice.

Membership Plans for Patients **Dr. A. Drew** (321–555–5555) adrewdo@conciergemed.com No private insurance All services are direct billed to patients	**Platinum Plan—$2,500 annual** • Family Plan, 2–3 enrollees living within the same household • 24/7 access to a board-certified physician • Inclusive annual physical for all enrollees • Paid in full annually
Gold Plan—$150 monthly • Individual Plan • 24/7 access to a board-certified physician • Inclusive annual physical • Paid in full on the 1st of each month, minimum 3 months	**Silver Plan—$90 monthly** • Individual Plan • 24/5, M–F access to a board-certified physician • Paid in full on the 1st of each month, minimum 5 months

SCENARIO ONE

The Ross family consists of four family members: a mother, father, and two children. Mr. and Mrs. Ross decide it is best for their family's needs to enroll in Dr. Drew's concierge practice. After reviewing Dr. Drew's website, the Ross family realizes the Platinum Plan allows a maximum of three enrollees, so they will have to tack on the Gold or Silver Plan to cover all four family members. Mr. Ross is very athletic and in his 40 years has rarely needed medical care, so they decide to contact Dr. Drew's practice and enroll in the Silver Plan along with the Platinum Plan.

As noted on the website, the enrollment process is to be completed through the online forms link housed within the website. However, Mrs. Ross calls the office line to further discuss her family's needs. Within two rings, Mrs. Ross is greeted by a friendly receptionist: "Thank you for calling Dr. Drew's Concierge Medicine, this is Janna, how can I help you today?" After a brief discussion and explanation of the family's needs, the receptionist offers to speak with Dr. Drew to see if any reasonable accommodation can be made.

Within 24 hours, the receptionist returns Mrs. Ross' call, delivering great news: Dr. Drew has offered to add the Ross' fourth family member to the Platinum Plan for an additional $800 annually, an upfront $280 savings for the family. Mrs. Ross is ecstatic, and before she can hang up to enroll online, the receptionist offers to complete the enrollment process immediately while they are on the phone. Mrs. Ross remits payment of the $3,300 annual fee and receives a confirmation email of their membership and receipt.

SCENARIO TWO

Matt is a bachelor who lives in an upscale area of the city. He has been a patient of Dr. Drew's for a number of years, enrolled under the Gold Plan. Over the past few years, Matt has called Dr. Drew to take advantage of his inclusive annual physical, which is part of his plan, and twice for symptoms that ended up testing positive for the flu virus. In general, Matt is a healthy guy who utilizes Dr. Drew's services for peace of mind and convenience in those what-if moments.

In the spring, Matt decided he would try his hand at a home improvement project to update his bachelor pad. The latest craze of having an accent wall wrapped in old barn wood seemed easy enough. After purchasing the wood along with a reciprocating saw, nail gun, nails, a level, and a tape measure, Matt decided to begin the project.

Halfway through the project, Matt was shaving a few inches off a corner board and the saw clipped his thumb. In an instant, he realized this was more than a scratch and would require stitches. Doubled over in pain, he reached for his phone and called Dr. Drew. His receptionist answered: "Thank you for calling Dr. Drew's Concierge Medicine, this is Janna, how can I help you today?" Janna asked a set of questions to determine the severity of the wound. Matt was placed on a brief hold and then was directed to wrap the wound in a clean towel and apply pressure to restrict the bleeding; Dr. Drew would be there shortly.

Within the hour, Dr. Drew was knocking at the door, medical bag in hand, dressed in slacks and a pristine lab coat. Immediately Dr. Drew prepared a sterile workstation on the kitchen table. Dr. Drew evaluated, cleaned, numbed, stitched, and dressed Matt's wound. Upon completion of his services, Dr. Drew set up his mobile printer and provided Matt with a hardcopy record of his visit, including a synopsis of wound care, charges to be billed, a follow-up appointment, and a prescription.

Matt sat on the couch while Dr. Drew cleaned his workstation. Before leaving, Dr. Drew offered to prepare Matt a glass of water and a fresh bag of ice for swelling. He reassured his patient to call if he needed anything and locked the doorknob before pulling the door shut on his way out.

SCENARIO THREE

Trisha is a recent college graduate at the beginning stages of her career working for an up-and-coming marketing firm. She works long hours, commutes from the suburbs to the firm four days a week, and offices out of home on Fridays. Trisha is a highly motivated employee; she is typically the first in and the last out. Unfortunately, the high-stress work environment and her determination often leave her exhausted and rundown. This type of lifestyle results in a weakened immune system, and therefore, Trisha is more susceptible to illness.

Waiting to schedule doctors' appointments, using valuable time to drive to the clinic, and then waiting to be seen in the dingy waiting room did not pair well with Trisha's need for efficiency. After a quick web search one weekend, Trisha realized Dr. Drew's concierge practice may be the most effective and efficient access to healthcare.

Trisha had to weigh the pros and cons of the Gold Plan versus the Silver Plan for her specific needs. The Gold Plan has 24/7 access to care, while the Silver is only five days a week. The annual physical was also a plus on the Gold Plan, but the $60 monthly difference could be used toward living or student loan expenses. After drawing up numerous comparisons, consulting her Excel budget and then working through a series of what-if scenarios, Trisha enrolled in the Silver Plan.

Within two months of her membership, Trisha had seen Dr. Drew on three occasions. Twice Dr. Drew came to her office and once to her home. Trisha, again, woke up one morning with sinus pressure and a throbbing pain in her ear coupled with a low-grade fever and a toothache. Immediately Trisha knew she was sick, and with an upcoming presentation the following week, it could not have been a more inconvenient time.

Scrambling for her phone, she realized it was Sunday and her membership, the Silver Plan, was Monday through Friday. Regardless, Trisha called Dr. Drew. His receptionist answered and placed her on a brief hold as she was working with another patient. A few moments later, his receptionist answered and explained that Dr. Drew could be to her house first thing Monday morning. Unsatisfied, Trisha insisted that Dr. Drew come that afternoon. The receptionist explained the terms of her membership and offered the solution that Trisha can terminate her agreement and switch to a higher membership, but she would be subject to both monthly fees as well as an early termination fee of her original contract.

Ultimately, Trisha decided to wait to see Dr. Drew that next morning. Dr. Drew arrived at the exact time he was scheduled; he was professional, courteous, and thorough. Upon completion of her appointment, Dr. Drew sat for a few moments to discuss the option to switch to the Gold Plan on the first of the next month to eliminate a duplicate fee and that he would waive the early termination fee if she decided to switch at that time.

Sources: http://www.aafp.org/about/policies/all/family-medicine-definition.html

http://health.usnews.com/health-news/hospital-of-tomorrow/articles/2014/04/01/physicians-abandon-insurance-for-blue-collar-concierge-model

DISCUSSION OUTLINE/QUESTION SET

1. Are all patients equally as valuable to the physician? Why or why not?

2. Analyze each physician-patient scenario. Through this analysis, determine which of the three additional elements of the marketing mix are most relevant to each. Explain.

3. How would offering different levels of membership alter the business model of Scenario One?

4. How do you perceive value? What membership plan best fits your needs? Why?

THE CHANGING HEALTHCARE MARKET

The internet is probably the most significant influence over changes in the healthcare market. For example, initially the internet was used primarily by consumers to search for their symptoms to determine a possible illness or disease or used as a search tool to find a physician or healthcare facility. However, as figure 3.3 illustrates, the internet now gives consumers and healthcare providers many new tools to assist in the actual care of patients. New technologies such as mobile apps that track vital signs, prescriptions, and fitness levels are now commonplace for patients and providers alike.

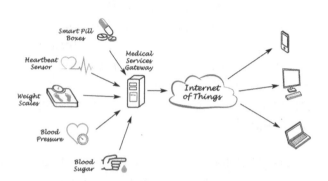

Figure 3.3 Brave New World—Telemedicine

The rising costs of healthcare have led many consumers to seek alternative treatments for healthcare problems. Consumers are now using essential oils, acupuncture, medical massage, and other homeopathic treatments to treat common ailments and even more serious medical conditions, as shown in Figure 3.4. Future changes in healthcare could include the expansion of health savings accounts (HSAs),

Figure 3.4 Changing Face of Healthcare

which now place consumers in complete charge of how they want to manage their medical problems. HSAs often include expenditures for alternative medical products and treatments, which further complicates the competitive environment of the healthcare market.

MEDICAL TOURISM

The travel industry dramatically changed with the increased consumer access to purchasing airline tickets, hotel rooms, rental cars, and travel packages. Figure 3.5 illustrates how healthcare is now facing similar paradigm shifts due to the ease of accessibility for consumers to multiple options with regard to healthcare delivery. It is imperative for any competitive analysis to consider the evolving competitive environment that has revolutionized the healthcare industry by offering consumers nontraditional options to address their healthcare needs. The healthcare market is definitely consumer-driven with regard to options and expectations of customization to consumers' individual needs. Table 3.1 compares the cost of medical procedures in the U.S. to costs a consumer could expect to pay abroad. If consumers use their HSAs to pay for their medical expenses, more consumers may opt to explore medical tourism due to the potential cost savings for certain medical procedures.

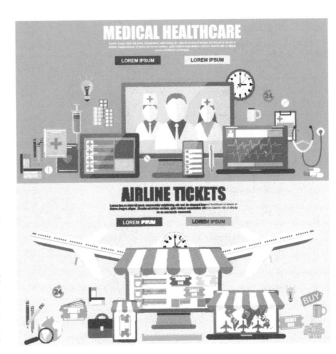

Figure 3.5 Medical Tourism

TABLE 3.1 MEDICAL TOURISM PRICING COMPARISONS

PROCEDURE	COST IN U.S.	COST ABROAD
Orthopedic		
Hip Replacement	$40,000–$65,000	$7,000–$13,000
Hip Resurfacing	$50,000–$60,000	$8,000–$12,000
Knee Replacement	$45,000–$60,000	$7,500–$12,000
Neurology		
Spinal Fusion	$80,000–$100,000	$6,000–$10,000
Total Spinal Disc Replacement	$100,000–$150,000	$8,000–$12,000
Discectomy	$20,000–$24,000	$5,000–$7,000
Cardiology		
Angioplasty	$50,000–$65,000	$5,000–$7,000
Heart Bypass	$90,000–$120,000	$10,000–$18,000
Heart Valve Replacement	$125,000–$175,000	$13,000–$18,000
Gynecology		
Hysterectomy	$18,000–$25,000	$4,000–$7,000
Cosmetic		
Face & Neck Lift	$8,000–$15,000	$2,500–$4,000
Breast Augmentation	$6,000–$12,000	$3,500–$5,000
Tummy Tuck	$6,000–$12,000	$3,800–$5,200
Liposuction/Area	$2,000–$3,000	$800–$1,200
Dental		
Dental Implants/Tooth	$3,000–$5,000	$800–$2,000
Dental Crowns	$800–$1,200	$200–$600

Source: http://www.medretreat.com/procedures/pricing.html

TELEMEDICINE

Heller (2016) discussed the increased usage of telemedicine and cited the Mercer National Survey, which found that 59% of employers offer a telemedicine program to their employees, an increase of 16% from 2014. The prevalence of telemedicine may be due in part to its lower costs and ease of access. Traditional office visits typically cost approximately $125, whereas a telemedicine office visit averages around $40. Because the number of high-deductible health insurance plans used by individuals has been increasing in recent years, telemedicine offers an affordable solution for consumers wanting to spend their healthcare dollars more efficiently. Additionally, many large companies are providing access to digital healthcare tools.

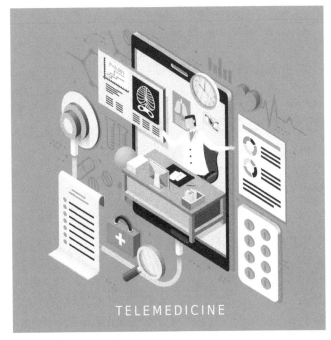

Figure 3.6 The Patient is In—Telemedicine

DIGITAL HEALTH TOOLS

The American Medical Association (2016) conducted a survey on digital health and found that 85% of physicians saw advantages to using digital tools to care for their patients. Primary care doctors were the group that saw the most advantage, although patient demand did not drive this acceptance. Physicians cited improved efficiency, increased patient safety, improved diagnostic ability, reduced burnout, and improvement in the patient-doctor relationship. The survey was administered to 1,300 U.S. primary care physicians and specialists ranging in age from 28 to 65 with a minimum of 20 hours of patient care per week. In this study, physicians listed the following "must haves" for their ability to adopt digital health tools:

1. Liability/malpractice coverage

2. Assured data privacy/security

3. HER workflow integration

4. Can be reimbursed

5. Intuitive—ease of use

READING SELECTIONS

READING 3.1

A REVOLUTION IN HEALTHCARE: MEDICINE MEETS THE MARKETPLACE

BY FRED HANSEN

Are we seeing a repeat of what happened to the media industry in healthcare? A wave of media-literate consumers, using a host of new Internet tools, powered a dismantling of the big media monopoly on public opinion. Healthcare could be next.

With competition nearly absent and with unchecked increases in demand over the last two decades, health markets in industrialised countries are undergoing intense change at tsunami-like speed, responding to levels of health expenditure that are growing twice as fast as the economy at large.

As both the quality of state-run health services and doctors' reimbursement for such services have declined, customers seem prepared to spend more cash for their own healthcare, taking control over expenditures to boot. The Canadian government, for example, spent US$87 billion on healthcare last year, but Canadian consumers added US$38 billion out of their own pockets.

Medical progress is not primarily to blame for exploding healthcare costs, as most such progress is paid for, by default, by the dominant third-party purchasers in healthcare such as governments, employers and insurers. It is telling that, before the introduction of Medicare in the 1960s, overall healthcare spending in the United States was only five per cent of the GDP. It now stands at 16 per cent and is projected to skyrocket to 25 per cent by 2030. The late Milton Friedman argued that healthcare

in all Western countries is still an anomaly, given that it has always been protected against otherwise pervasive and successful market forces.

Indeed, market dominance by governments and third parties in Western countries is so great that there is scarce competition in healthcare over prices and quality. Private insurers are simply following the path of state-run healthcare, stifling entrepreneurship and innovation. The situation is already precarious given that attempts to control costs over the last decades have been largely unsuccessful.

This year, for the first time ever, the imminent meltdown of U.S. Medicare has been suggested. The main reason for this is that all the reforms so far undertaken have addressed only the demand side of the market. The strange thing here is that buyers are telling sellers/providers how to practice medicine. We are talking about practice guidelines, preferred provider organisations (PPOs), managed care, health maintenance organisations (HMOs), and, more recently, health savings accounts (HSAs). Their effects are limited as long as doctors are not free to re-bundle and re-price health services and compete for customers.

In the U.S., for example, state regulations do not allow no-frills basic health insurance. Instead, they require insurance to cover anything from genetic tests and chiropractics, to acupuncture, marriage counselling, or artificial insemination. Furthermore, insurers have to stick to community rating and guaranteed issues, which means that everyone has to be accepted and pays the same premium. There is, therefore, no possibility for proper risk-management. The result is unaffordable private insurance, which in turn has prompted more Americans to opt out of health insurance altogether. There is good evidence that, over the last decade, the steepest increase among uninsured Americans has occurred in the bracket of families well above the poverty level. People just seem to think that they don't get their money's worth with the available insurance packages.

Increasingly, waiting for doctors has become the prevailing form of rationing in the West: mild in the U.S., moderate in Australia and severe in Canada and the UK. This, in turn, has created millions of frustrated customers who have begun to look elsewhere. The Internet and cheap airfares have greatly increased consumers' opportunities and choices by creating new consumer-driven markets. Cosmetic surgery, retail walk-in clinics, boutique medicine, Internet pharmacies, and international medical tourism are only some examples. These areas, where the state and other third-party agencies are absent, are bristling with innovation and entrepreneurship: on a global scale, nurses and doctors are busy rebundling and repackaging their services at competitive (and often lower) prices. Over the last decade, free competition has brought down the prices in cosmetic surgery by up to 30 per cent. Furthermore, a growing number of high-quality healthcare facilities in developing countries are catering for so-called medical tourists from industrialised countries, among them many uninsured Americans. Services abroad are, on average, 80 per cent cheaper according to the founders of PlanetHospital. Their data show that heart surgery which costs more than $50,000 in the United States can be purchased for $20,000 in Singapore, for $12,000 in Thailand, and between $3,000 and $10,000 in India. Though one may have doubts about the quality and safety of such a heavily discounted heart procedure, the success rate of coronary bypass surgery in India is reported to be 98.7 percent as against 97.5 percent in the U.S. Already, people can receive most major or complex procedures abroad. The competition is on, and most hospitals catering for the international market have either passed Western accreditation standards or are attempting to do so.

According to McKinsey & Company, India's health industry, one of the most promising in the field, is expected to grow from its present size of just US$25 billion to a whopping $190 billion in less than two decades. Many observers of the global healthcare industry are expecting that, in the coming decade, the increasing pressure on the supply of healthcare will set off a tsunami of health consumerism of sorts. Although up from 500,000 in 2006 to 750,000 in 2007, the number of Americans travelling abroad for healthcare is tipped to increase to 6 million by 2010.

There are plenty of signs of emerging global market responses to the Western supply crisis. The market for medical tourism was worth $60 billion in 2006 and is rapidly growing. Again, according to McKinsey & Company, it could rise to $100 billion by 2012. Big insurers are already adding global low-cost providers to their health plan networks. Blue Shield of California, for instance, allows enrolees of its health plan to have access to cheaper physicians across the Mexican border. Blue Cross of South Carolina allows treatment at the Bumrungrad International Hospital in Thailand, which treated 400,000 foreigners in the last year, including 80,000 Americans. Furthermore, India and China are already major suppliers of low-cost drugs and drug ingredients to U.S. consumers, as the recent scandal over poisoned or toxic imports has revealed. India alone produces 350 varieties of antidepressants, heart medicines, antibiotics, and other drugs purchased by Americans. Last year, China sold pharmaceuticals worth $670 million on the U.S. market. The downside is that the risks to human health are also growing quickly and the U.S. Food and Drug Administration is struggling to catch up, having conducted roughly 200 inspections of plants in China and India over the last seven years.

But there are even more instances of consumer-driven changes pushing for supply side reforms to health markets:

- Growing numbers of consumers are not willing to put up with the rationing-by-waiting for a doctor anymore and are paying out-of-pocket to jump the queue in industrialised countries. For instance, in Australia, patients are paying up to $600 for private treatment to avoid queues at crowded public hospital emergency departments. At Sydney Adventist Hospital, which has the largest private emergency section in NSW, doctors see 21,000 such patients per year. Australian dental tours to Thailand are already very popular.
- Web-based online patient networks and mailing lists are becoming an increasingly powerful force. One of the biggest is the U.S.-based Association of Cancer Online Resources (ACOR) with 159 online cancer groups. Increasing numbers of people with health problems are looking for help on the Internet, as 5.4 million Americans purchased drugs from other countries over the Internet last year.

THE INTERNET AND CHEAP AIRFARES HAVE GREATLY INCREASED CONSUMERS' OPPORTUNITIES AND CHOICES BY CREATING NEW CONSUMER-DRIVEN MARKETS.

- Another market response to hospital waiting lists is Internet-based services for medical expertise framed as a second opinion. Once a full patient record has been submitted, for a fee of $450, Connected Health grants access to 4,000 medical specialists. This is probably good value for the money. A 2003 review by the *British Medical Journal* showed that working diagnoses changed in only five percent of cases, but that, in 90 percent of cases, new treatment alternatives were developed.

- Triggered by the 2003 U.S.-wide introduction of new tax-free health savings accounts (HSAs), about 1,000 banks entered the healthcare market by offering health coverage and developing new consumer models: U.S. uptake of HSAs has surged from 1 million in 2005 to 3.5 million in 2006 and is expected to reach 10 million by 2008. With plenty of cash for health purchases, HSAs are fuelling the global market for medical tourism. Big U.S. health insurers, such as United Health and Blue Cross/Blue Shield, have gained bank charters to get into the HSA market.

- In the face of an expected primary care physicians shortage of 200,000 over the coming decade, U.S. retailers are responding with nurse-led and GP-backed (1 for 4) walk-in clinics. Five hundred of these are already operating across the United States. RediClinic, one of the new providers, is reported to have a 97 percent patient satisfaction rating. Wal-Mart has announced that it will open such clinics in 2,000 of its outlets; Walgreens and CVS Pharmacies have purchased national retail clinic chains.

- In the UK, the NHS has responded in kind, opening walk-in centres with extended hours for patients who cannot gain access to their GPs. Private providers are also setting up walk- in clinics. Research has shown that people aged under 34 years old—that is, the next generation of healthcare consumers—are less loyal to their GPs than their parents' generation and instead prefer fast access to walk-in clinics.

- Doctors are responding to rising out-of-pocket budgets for medical care by converting their traditional practices into "boutique" medical practices. Rather than the old-fashioned episodic and inefficient fee-for-service model, the boutique practice offers chronic patients (such as diabetics) care packages worth $1,500 for a whole year's medical service.

- U.S. employers, who had taken the brunt of rising health care costs over the last decades, are quietly shifting costs to employees through premium increases, higher deductibles, or more out-of-pocket payments. New consumer-driven healthcare plans in the U.S., while still a small percentage, are expected to triple in the next five years.

- Healthcare tourism is expanding in Europe, with German and English patients opting to pay a third or a half of what they pay at home by travelling to Warsaw or Budapest for dental work. Patients have been travelling across Europe for years to obtain major procedures at lower costs. The European Court of Justice ruled a couple of years ago that these countries should mutually reimburse such services.

- Offering dental work at one-fifth of U.S. prices and inexpensive drugs, Mexico is attracting the majority of American medical travellers. New hospitals have opened in Tijuana since some U.S. health plans are now covering services in Mexico. Stomach surgery, eye exams, and routine checkups are among the major services that Americans are seeking in Mexico. This is thanks to a legal system in Mexico that makes it almost impossible to sue dentists.
- In the interest of huge cost savings, U.S. insurance products such as "Mini-med" plans allow a limited number of doctor visits in the U.S. each year, with a much higher allowance in visits elsewhere. As a mini-med provider, PlanetHospital will cover all costs, including travel arrangements and treatment abroad for heart surgery for only $10,000.

These fledgling new health markets might finally undermine and outperform the behemoths of state-run health care, which only rarely use their purchasing power to benefit consumers. Walk-in customers, Internet drug buyers, and healthcare tourists are building up pressure on providers in industrialised countries for more transparency in the quality and the prices of services, and finally for more consumer choices. One may be forgiven for thinking that this, of course, reflects the long-held conviction by classical liberals that markets perform better than governments in allocating resources, and are much faster to respond to the demands of consumers. Patients are realising that the power of the consumer vote, exercised many times every day on choices in different markets, is incomparably better than one political vote and a blank cheque to politicians every four years.

READING 3.2

"ALTERNATIVE" HEALTHCARE: ACCESS AS A REVENUE SOURCE IN A CONSUMER-DRIVEN MARKET

BY A. MICHAEL LAPENNA

When "alternative" is paired with "healthcare," these terms come to mind: acupuncture, massage, herbal medicine, or some other nontraditional approaches to health and wellness. The message not often conveyed by the term "alternative healthcare"

A. Michael LaPenna, "'Alternative' Healthcare: Access as a Revenue Source in a Consumer-Driven Market," *Journal of Healthcare Management*, vol. 55, no. 1, pp. 7-10. Copyright © 2010 by Health Administration Press. Reprinted with permission. Provided by ProQuest LLC. All rights reserved.

is retail medicine, workplace medical clinic, telemedicine, medical tourism, or any other innovations in healthcare delivery. Yet these nontraditional access points to care have, more or less, become part of the landscape of a consumer-directed healthcare marketplace (see LaPenna 2009a; 2009b). In addition, the Internet has become a ubiquitous (if still not standard) player in accessing healthcare, used by people as "a means to accelerate the pace of discovery, widen social networks, and sharpen the questions someone might ask when they do get to talk to a health professional" (Fox 2009).

The lesson here for healthcare executives is to be cognizant of a simple fact: Most of the available alternative access points are disconnected from the provider networks and other resources that your organization spent many years and lots of capital to develop. Watch the environment closely, and seize the opportunities it presents.

PARTNERSHIP BETWEEN HOSPITALS AND RETAILERS

Collaborations between healthcare organizations and retailers are not new. Over the years, many major stores have given money to hospitals, clinics, health departments, and health/safety-related programs in exchange for various goods or services, including a better image in the community.

In the past few years, a new kind of exchange has taken place between healthcare and retail, especially between drugstores and hospitals. For example, Minute Clinic—a Joint Commission–accredited retail clinic that operates primarily in CVS Pharmacies—has partnered with Cleveland Clinic and Allina Health Systems to provide healthcare services. National chain Wal-Mart has also formed retail-clinic collaborations with health systems and community hospitals. Walgreens, through its Take Care Clinics, partners with several healthcare organizations. Recently, Walgreens signed a deal with Sarasota Memorial Hospital to deliver prescription medication to patients and staff on-site (*Tampa Bay Business Journal* 2009).

Convenience, lower cost, and integrated health records have been touted as the advantages for healthcare consumers. In addition, for many patients, a retail clinic is a better alternative to an overcrowded emergency department. For healthcare organizations, these partnerships represent a new source of capital. They may also serve to channel patients. Critics may call this strategy "cream skimming," especially if the organization just built an urgent care facility or an after-hours practice in between a CVS and a Walgreens.

HIGH-TECH, MOBILE HEALTHCARE

Forward thinking organizations have stretched the concept of the simple ambulance to enhance and support their services and programs and to facilitate the community's access to their facilities specifically or to healthcare generally. Among the many outgrowths in this area are the mobile healthcare clinic, mobile critical care unit, and air transport. This past summer, the AIDS Healthcare Foundation deployed an HIV- screening van to provide free tests to residents of 14 cities across the United States *(Business Wire* 2009). Similar mobile outreach has occurred throughout the history of healthcare delivery.

Many emergency vehicles or ambulances today are equipped with sophisticated diagnostic and treatment power as well as modem communication systems. In Indiana, electronic medical information capability has been added aboard a fleet of emergency vehicles, enabling technicians "to obtain vital patient health history by accessing their hospital medical records" (Wishard Health Services 2009). The same will be true for mobile healthcare units, which make health services accessible to those in rural and underserved areas and those with limited or no means of transportation. Will a mobile platform replace retail clinics, and what will this mean for the traditional "house call"?

Given these possibilities, high-tech ambulances and mobile units staffed by a team of well-trained providers (e.g., nurse practitioners, physician assistants, registered nurses, paramedics, lab technicians) could become another "convenience clinic" alternative for obtaining primary care services and hence a viable revenue source. Certainly, mobile healthcare providers are already in operation, but the trend has focused on mobile or remote monitoring and communications (i.e., telemedicine), not necessarily on physical access, diagnosis, and treatment.

MEDICAL TRANSMITTERS AND REMOTE MEDICINE

Although it offers numerous benefits, telemedicine has taken a back seat to many other investment priorities. Several factors in today's environment—including the aging of the population and shortage of primary care physicians, especially in rural areas—could accelerate telemedicine's adoption by health systems and hospitals, or at least open possibilities for new sources of revenue.

First, advances in technology make medical transmitters more sophisticated. "Machine-to-machine communications" enable better and faster electronic exchange of patient data. Recently, the U.S. Food and Drug Administration approved a wireless medical transmitter for patients with cardiac implants. Also, the Wii Fit—an interactive exercise videogame for the Wii console developed by Nintendo—has emerged as the first consumer-deployed medical transmitter. "Consumer deployed" means that this system was not pushed by healthcare providers or marketers but was pulled by consumers. The Wii Fit can take personal health data such as body mass index, record physical activities performed outside of the videogame, and design and monitor exercises. In addition, personal health electronic records may be "hooked up" to the Wii Fit, as may more sophisticated electronic medical information systems (for more information, see Games for Health at www.gamesforhealth.org).

Other nonhealthcare companies, such as Cisco and Cerner, are also leading in the telemedicine/telehealth field, developing transponder units, televideo systems, and monitoring packages that enhance traditional healthcare delivery but offer alternative access. In early 2009, a fully operational telemedicine program was unveiled in Antarctica that supports the on-site physicians and physician assistants who treat scientists, researchers, and other workers on the continent. The program, which relies on telephones, e-mails, video-conferencing units, and electronic medical records, links providers in Antarctica to a group of emergency physicians and specialists in Washington, DC (Reuters 2009).

Second, the American Recovery and Reinvestment Act of 2009 earmarked $2.5 billion in grants to organizations that develop and improve their broadband infrastructure in support of telemedicine programs. Grants have also been made available to rural hospitals and clinics for the purpose of expanding telecommunications capabilities that usher in remote medicine. These are no longer speculative programs. In select situations, traditional reimbursement channels are authorizing payment to doctors who provide care to patients through a television screen rather than in an exam room.

CONCLUSION

Consider the following:

- Estimates suggest that four in ten adults and one in ten children routinely partake in some type of complementary and alternative medicine, from consuming probiotics or St. John's Wort to doing yoga to going to a chiropractor.
- Wii Fit is so popular that its maker has launched Wii Fit Plus, an expanded version of the original.
- Mayo Clinic links its Minnesota-based specialists with outposts in Arizona and Florida.
- Numerous health systems sponsor and brand ambulance and patient transport units.
- Walgreens (2009) has teamed up with AARP to offer free health screening with ten mobile units that are scheduled to visit some 3,000 communities over the span of the project.

At the heart of these developments is the modem healthcare consumer, who spots and responds quickly to trends that allow convenient, comprehensive, quality, and (relatively) low-cost access to services and products. Consumers are increasingly in control of their own healthcare, and, more often than not, they elect to access care for the first time through alternative channels. The healthcare organization that understands these forces and molds them into a sustainable customer-focused strategy will greatly benefit.

REFERENCES

Business Wire. 2009. "AHF/Magic Johnson Testing Van to Host Free HIV Testing Event at Univ. of W. Florida." [Online article; retrieved 12/1/09.] www.aegis.com/NEWS/BW/2009/BW090619.html.

Fox, S. 2009. "The Social Life of Health Information." Pew Internet and American Life Project. [Online abstract; retrieved 12/1/09.] www.pewinterent.org/Reports/2009/8-The-Social-Life-of-Health-Information.aspx.

LaPenna, M. 2009a. "New Sources of Revenue in the Age of Connectivity." *Journal of Healthcare Management* 54 (1): 11–30.

_____. 2009b. "Workplace Medical Clinics: The Employer-Redesigned 'Company Doctor'." *Journal of Healthcare Management* 54 (2): 87–91.

Reuters. 2009. "Remote Medicine: GWU Medical Faculty Treat Antarctica Personnel." [Online article; retrieved 12/1/09.] www.reuters.com/article/iduS254256+26-Feb-2009+PRN20090226.

Tampa Bay Business Journal. 2009. "Sarasota Memorial and Walgreens Partner for Bedside Delivery." [Online article; retrieved 12/1/09.] http://tampabay.bizjournals.com/tampabay/stories/2009/11/09/daily32.html.

Walgreens. 2009. "AARP and Walgreens Launch Two-Year National Wellness Tour to Provide Free Health Screenings and Services." [Online news release; retrieved 12/1/09.] http://news.walgreens.com/article_display.cfm?article_id=5177.

Wishard Health Services. 2009. "Wishard Hospital EMS Vehicles First to Install Vital Regenstrief Medical Records System." [Online news release; retrieved 12/1/09.] www.medicine.indiana.edu/news_releases/viewRelease.php4?art=1114.

READING 3.3

MEDICAL TOURISM: A NEW VENUE OF HEALTHCARE

BY ALYSSA R. GOLDBACH AND DANIEL J. WEST, JR.

ABSTRACT

Medical tourism is a dynamic subset of global healthcare that incorporates a variety of services, procedures, and venues of care. Medical tourism encompasses both the inmigration of patients to the United States and the outsourcing of patients to international locations. Health insurance coverage, the impact on domestic and global markets, and the use of international standards of care will be examined in combination with quality, access, and cost parameters. The global nature of medical tourism invites a variety of legal and ethical issues and calls for an organizational body to monitor this new phenomenon. Finally, the future implications of the globalization of health services and systems will be discussed.

INTRODUCTION

Medical tourism is the movement of patients through a global network of health services. Medical tourists seek affordable healthcare on a timely basis in a variety of destination nations (Turner, 2007). The expansion of global medical services has sparked immense economic growth in developing nations and has created a new market for advertising access to care. Beyond offering a unique untapped market of services, medical tourism has invited a host of liability, malpractice, and ethical concerns. The explosion of offshore "mini-surgical" vacations will surely incite global unification and increased access, quality, and affordability of care.

Approximately 750,000 Americans traveled to India, Singapore, Thailand, and variety of other locations for medical procedures ranging from dental work to cardiovascular surgery in 2007 (Keckley & Underwood, 2008). These medical tourists are seeking care at an affordable rate, sometimes up to seventy percent cheaper than in the United States, in combination with luxuries of staying in a resort, often in a tropical location (Keckley & Underwood, 2008). Beyond the outsourcing of health services from the United States, medical tourism also encompasses inbound travel to the United States and travel within the country. It is estimated that 417,000 people entered the United States for healthcare in 2007, with most of these procedures occurring at large research institutes, teaching hospitals, and other well-known hospitals (Keckley & Underwood, 2008).

Strong economic growth in developing countries has sparked an intense market for medical tourism. Through new resources and the extension of American based hospitals such as Johns Hopkins Hospital, The Cleveland Clinic, and Harvard Medical Center the market for outbound medical tourism is expected to grow to from $60 million in 2006 to $100 billion dollars by 2010 (Keckley & Underwood, 2008). Affiliation with U.S.-based hospitals ensures consumer safety and a higher caliber of care; however, liability, malpractice, and ethical concerns arise when patients return to the United States to seek post-surgical treatment for procedures performed by different physicians outside of the United States. A variety of Internet based companies, travel agencies, and medical travel planners appreciate the implications of this marketing venture. Thus, they have developed plans to aid patients in seeking adequate care and treatment abroad (Keckley & Underwood, 2008).

Medical tourism presents a new generation of healthcare that globally integrates a variety of services, procedures, and venues. At a lower cost, with certified physicians, medical tourism is likely to grow as patients seek more affordable, equitable care abroad. The combination of United States facilities with those abroad and the possibilities of health insurance coverage outside of the United States will likely aid in the explosion of medical tourism (Keckley & Underwood, 2008). Integration will hopefully precipitate global unification and cooperation of personnel to achieve optimum patient care. Medical tourism is a rapidly growing phenomenon and a unique sector of the healthcare industry of the future.

MEDICAL TOURISM

Wealthy patients have been traveling to the United States and other highly advanced countries to seek premier healthcare for many years. American hospitals, such as Harvard Medical Center and Johns Hopkins, are known for their innovative techniques and extraordinary care, thus attracting international patients. Inmigration of patients to the United States noticeably began in the 1960s and has steadily increased in popularity until 9/11 (Schroth and Khawaja, 2007). Since then, inmigration has slowed and possibly leveled off from other countries.

Historically a few Americans have traveled abroad, to less prestigious nations, for cheaper cosmetic procedures and for procedures not covered by insurance in the United States. There is an explosion of patients from the United States traveling in the reverse direction, to "developing" countries, for service such as orthopedic procedures, heart surgery, dental work, experimental drugs, and access to technology. "Developing" countries refers to low-income and middle-income economies as calculated by the World Bank Atlas Method (The World Bank). This method divides countries based on income groups. The income groups are: low income, $975 or less; lower middle income, $976–$3,855; upper middle income, $3,856–$11,905; and high income, $11,906 or more GNI per capita (The World Bank). These groups are characterized by operational lending categories by the World Bank (The World Bank).

COUNTRY	NUMBER OF JCI ACCREDITED HOSPITALS	WORLD BANK CLASSIFICATION
India	10	Lower middle income
Thailand	4	Lower middle income
Singapore	13	Low income
Malaysia	1	Upper middle income
South Africa	None	Upper middle income
Brazil	12	Upper middle income
Costa Rica	1	Upper middle income
Mexico	3	Upper middle income
Hungary	None	High income
United Arab Emirates	25	High income
Saudi Arabia	29	High income
Argentina	None	Upper middle income
Philippines	2	Lower middle income
Turkey	35	Upper middle income
El Salvador	None	Lower middle income

Figure 3.7 Most Popular Countries for Medical Tourism

Figure 3.7 illustrates the most popular medical tourism destinations and the number of Joint Commission International Hospitals located there (Keckley &Underwood, 2008; The World Bank).

"Developing" countries offer care at a significantly decreased rate, often in combination with luxury vacation. The concept of medical tourism is not new. Patients have been traveling globally for care for the past half-century.

Since 2002, it appears a mass migration for certain health services out of the United States is underway given the cost of care, lack of coverage for specific services, and the inability to access specific procedures in the United States.

INFLUX TO THE UNITED STATES

UNITED STATES FACILITIES

Leading United States facilities have long attracted foreign patients with their research, technology, and their prestigious reputations for excellence. It is estimated that 417,000 people entered the United States for care in 2007, with most of these procedures occurring at large research institutes and well-known hospitals (Keckley & Underwood, 2008). The most popular procedures can be categorized into cardiovascular, orthopedic, oncologic, and cosmetic (Keckley & Underwood, 2008). These procedures often begin with virtual counseling in which telemedicine is used to confirm that care is needed in the United States (Keckley & Underwood, 2008). This is followed by care in the United States, either by a referred physician or a patient transfer of an affiliated American Medical center or healthcare network (Keckley & Underwood, 2008). This process offers a glimpse into the opportunities that United States hospitals offer in both attracting and treating foreign patients.

REASONS FOR TRAVEL TO THE UNITED STATES

Beyond the outsourcing of health services from the United States, medical tourism also encompasses inbound travel to the United States and travel within the country. The majority of patient inmigration to the United States involves complex surgery that requires major medical intervention and a significant stay in the United States. Patients from South American, European, and Middle Eastern countries arrive in the United States for a variety of healthcare reasons. A large percentage of inbound tourists arrive to avoid excessive delays in the universal healthcare system and achieve highly specialized care (Keckley & Underwood, 2008). Patients from Mexico often enter in search of emergency care without the high price tag that they would incur in Mexico (Keckley & Underwood, 2008). Others seek procedures unavailable in their home country. Overall, migrants to the United States are seeking access to high quality and positive outcomes for their medical ailments. The open access healthcare system in the United States allows people from socialist and universal healthcare systems to receive care more quickly than they would in their homeland.

International affiliations with United States facilities have aided in inbound medical tourism by increasing the knowledge and availability of care abroad (Keckley & Underwood, 2008). Medical directories and foreign physicians trained in the United States have also aided in increasing the awareness of medical tourism in the United States (Keckley & Underwood, 2008). Overall, inbound medical tourism is expected to slightly increase and maintain at a steady rate over the next decade (Keckley & Underwood, 2008).

MIGRATION OF PATIENTS OUT OF THE UNITED STATES

OUTSOURCING FACILITIES AND PROCEDURES

Medical tourists visit a variety of countries that encircle the globe. Thailand, India, and Singapore represent some of the most popular destinations. Together, these nations house 27 Joint Commission International (JCI) accredited hospitals. In total, the JCI has accredited over 200 international institutions in 39 countries (JCI). The most popular procedures sought in these countries are dental, cosmetic, cardiovascular, and orthopedic (Keckley & Underwood, 2008). Still, other tourists travel to the Middle Eastern, South American, and Caribbean countries to seek care types of treatment not found in the United States.

MOTIVES FOR CARE ABROAD

Patients often seek care abroad for the financial discount. Others see the vacation possibility with medical tourism. The idea of having low risk surgery while relaxing at a luxury beachfront resort also aids in enticing some tourists. Other destinations offer visits to historical sites or national landmarks as part of the medical tourism package (Turner, 2007). Most medical tourism destinations offer beachside access in tropical locations to patients seeking "sun, sand and surgery" (Connell, 2006). Others lack insurance and offshore surgery presents the only way for people to receive a necessary procedure at an affordable price. Still others are attempting to avoid excessive wait times for elective procedures in their home nations. In nations like Canada and some European countries, universal healthcare creates a backup of procedures especially those that are elective, or nonlife-threatening. New medical technologies and innovative procedures are also used to lure patients abroad (Turner, 2007). Procedures and experimental drugs not offered in the United States aid in encouraging patients to seek care out of the United States.

As many United States companies outsource jobs and facilities, the Americans following them seek adequate care. Multinational companies expect their employees to receive high quality care. This type of "transitional" care presents a new phenomenon in which the high-quality demand of Americans is generating an increase in accreditation and certification of foreign hospitals. In an attempt to lure patients and exemplify quality, foreign hospitals are seeking all outlets to ensure patients that their facility is a safe and secure place. Insurance companies have also begun to offer abroad options for surgery, at reduced fee in addition to travel benefits (Schroth & Khawaja, 2007).

A bill was introduced in the House of Representative in 2006, to offer financial incentives to state employees willing to travel abroad (Turner, 2007). The bill proposed waiving copayments deductibles, reimbursement for travel expenses, seven complimentary sick days, and even a financial reward (Turner, 2007). West Virginia is one of many states proposing this option to cut the financial deficits they are facing.

Insurance companies and other corporations are offering abroad healthcare options at a reduced fee.

SAVINGS

The savings abroad on procedures can be up to 50% that of procedures within the United States. This amazing savings is the driving force for medical tourism. Medical tourists also have to factor in the cost of travel and stay in their "destination nation" (Turner, 2007). Travel for surgery incurs many additional costs than surgery at home does. Patients should be aware of this when calculating the actual savings of going abroad for healthcare. Patients must also consider the risks of going abroad in terms of the possibility of errors in care. Legal issues can arise once the patient returns home and medical complications develop. If this occurs, the patient has to spend even more money to repair and/or reverse the mistakes made abroad by another healthcare provider, and access to legal recourse is minimal.

PROCEDURE	COST IN THE UNITED STATES (OUTPATIENT) IN U.S. DOLLARS	COST IN THE UNITED STATES (INPATIENT) IN U.S. DOLLARS	AVERAGE COST ABROAD IN U.S. DOLLARS	PERCENT SAVINGS (OUTPATIENT)
Rhinoplasty	3,866	5,713	2,156*	55%
Knee Surgery	4,686	11,692	1,398*	70%
Shoulder Angioplasty	8,972	6,720	2,493*	72%
Hysterectomy	6,132	6,542	2,114*	66%
Tubal Ligation	3,894	6,407	1,412*	64%
Haemorrhoidectomy	2,354	5,594	884*	62%
Bunionectomy	2,706	6,840	1,682	35%
Glaucoma procedures	2,593	4,392	1,151	56%
Varicose Vein Surgery	2,685	7,993	1,576	41%
Cataract Extraction	2,630	4,067	1,282	51%
Skin Lesion Excision	1,919	7,059	919	53%
Hernia Repair	3,903	5,377	1,819	53%
Adult Tonsillectomy	2,185	3,844	1,143	48%

Figure 3.8 The Savings of Medical Tourism
*Average of Cost abroad was taken from three lowest foreign prices and includes travel costs in U.S. dollars.

Figure 3.8 describes the cost of popular outpatient procedures both in the United States and abroad. Percent savings is illustrated for all outpatient procedures (Keckley & Underwood, 2008).

The savings of medical tourism varies among countries and is often indicative of quality of care. Starkly lower prices should signal to patients that quality is not a premium. Surgery should not be something that a patient puts on hold in order to access tourist locations. In a changing world, where insurance dictates medical procedures, more and more patients are seeking care at an affordable rate; even if that means cross-continental care.

LEGAL HURDLES

Malpractice and privacy issues comprise two of the most important legal factors in medical tourism. Malpractice issues arise when a patient returns to the United States marred, disfigured, or having other detrimental health conditions as a result of procedures done "offshore." It then becomes the responsibility of United States physicians to help the patient. Some physicians are reluctant to assume high-risk care caused by negligence from a foreign physician.

Privacy issues arise when medical records have to be electronically sent around the world so that physicians can communicate. Digitalizing medical records enables more people to access them and limits patient privacy protection. Privacy laws in different countries also limit the ways in which patient privacy can be protected. HIPAA regulators, that protect patient rights in the United States, often do not exist in foreign countries. This allows sensitive information about personal and private medical conditions to be easily transmitted among hospital staff and other related personnel. This loss of confidentiality is critical. The WHO has set up a committee to identify and clarify the role of technology in patient safety around the world and develop future direction for an alliance of technology for patient safety (WHO). Currently, the Stark laws prevent physicians from referring patients to abroad hospitals, which also limits their degree of control in the situation (Turner, 2007). This hinders the physician's ability to help the patient choose a safe and appropriate hospital in another country.

Foreign laws regarding liability are not as strict as those in the United States, which leads to decreased malpractice compensation (Herrick, 2007). Injured patients may find legal recourse difficult in a foreign court or may have no rights at all regarding the error in their procedure. A set of international law concerning medical liability has yet to be agreed upon and approved by of all the nations involved (Schroth and Khawaja, 2007). The Universal Declaration of Bioethics and Human Rights by the WHO, the Declaration of Helsinki by the World Medical Association (WMA), and the Good Clinical Practice by International Conference on Harmonisation (ICH) are some of the attempts to institute international law. None of these declarations are legally binding and often cannot be enforced but they are understood as a universal code of ethics for the treatment of human beings. The lack of international quality standards is partially due to the lack of an international authoritative body to enforce the standards (WHO). Lack of coordination, organization, and participation of nations around the world also contributes to the inability to enforce international standards (WHO).

Often, decreased cost of care infers a lesser quality of quality of care, as the phrase "First World Healthcare at Third World Prices" suggests (Turner, 2007). All "offshore" hospitals do not necessarily follow the same quality standards. External reviews, facilitators such as United States hospital affiliates, and organizations such as JCI and the WHO aid in regulating and managing care abroad. Currently the JCI includes over 300 foreign hospitals (JCI). The JCI also monitors quality and accredits international facilities. Several international countries have established their own certification bodies to ensure quality (Turner, 2007). The JCI, though, remains the dominant and most recognizable accreditation body in the world (Turner, 2007). Brand identification among prestigious United States hospital affiliates is often essential to quality assurance and patient recognition. Often, "offshore" hospitals employ physicians trained in the United States, Canada, Australia, or the United Kingdom and United States board certified physicians (Turner, 2007). United States and British flags on an international hospital website also aid in ensuring customers of quality.

ORGANIZATION NAME	TYPE OF REGULATION
JCI (Joint Commission International)	Areas of Accreditation and Certification: Ambulatory Care, Clinical Laboratory, Disease and Condition Specific, Hospital, Medical Transport, Primary Care
WHO (World Health Organization)	International Health Regulators
ISQUA (The International Society for Quality in Healthcare)	Quality healthcare for all, Responsiveness, Innovation, Achieving, Integrity, Stewardship
NCQA (National Committee for Quality Assurance)	Accreditation, certification, recognition

Figure 3.9 International Regulators of Healthcare Quality

Figure 3.9 depicts the organizations who aim to regulate international healthcare facilities to ensure patient safety and quality of care (JCI; WHO; ISQUA; NCQA).

An initiative, called Healthcare Quality Indicator (HCQI) developed by the Organization for Economic Cooperation and Development (OECD) aims to develop international measures of quality (Schroth and Khawaja, 2007). HCQI is focused on healthcare needs, effectiveness, safety, and responsiveness (OECD). The committee is made of representatives from 23 countries (OECD). A lack of international standards of care also hinder quality control but other initiatives such that by the World Health Organization aims to strengthen healthcare safety and monitoring (Schroth and Khawaja, 2007).

FACILITATORS

MEDIATORS

Many organizations have seen the growth of medical tourism as an entrepreneurial prospect. Organizations that aid patients in finding surgery abroad and assisting them with the entire medical travel experience have become very popular. Medical brokerages such as Plant Hospital, Global Choice Healthcare, Med Journeys and Med Retreat have emerged as leaders of the medical travel planners (Turner, 2007). These businesses aid patients from finding a physician and hospital to arranging hotel and travel accommodations to finalizing their return home to the United States. Often, these planners offer a "menu" of services from which prospective patients can choose (Turner, 2007).

ORGANIZATION NAME	SERVICES PROVIDED	DESTINATION LOCATIONS
MedRetreat www.medretreat.com	Step-by-step guide for medical tourists, includes pre-counseling, travel information, financial advice, and travel "tips" and "necessities"	Argentina, Brazil, Costa Rica, El Salvador, India, Malaysia, Mexico, South Africa, Thailand, Turkey
Planet Hosptial www.planethospital.com	Hospitals include many American extension institutions, offers medical tourism insurance, aids in planning from airfare to return home	Argentina, Belguim, Brazil, Costa Rica, El Salvador, India, Mexico, Panama, Philippines, Singapore, South Korea, Thailand
Med Journeys www.medjourneys.com	All-inclusive and VIP packages offered, Lists 16 step guidelines for entire journey	Mexico, Costa Rica, Brazil, Poland, Turkey, India, Thailand, Malaysia, Singapore
Healthbase www.healthbase.com	Partnered with various travel agencies, lists step-by-step guide to travel, affiliated with American extension hospitals, travel insurance, loan processing partner with various banks	Mexico, Costa Rica, Turkey, India, Thailand, Malaysia, Singapore, Philippines, South Korea, Belgium, Hungary, Panama, Brazil, United States

Figure 3.10 Internet Mediators of Medical Tourism

Figure 3.10 illustrates the "menu" of services and destinations from which prospective patients can choose from medical planners (Turner, 2007).

They often offer a variety of medical tourism destinations at a variety of price ranges for the consumer to choose from, with each destination offering different amenities (Turner, 2007). Medical travel planners must assure patients that the benefits of traveling abroad outweigh the risks and that quality of care will be maintained.

Insurance companies, such as Aetna, have even offered abroad care options. Other major health insurance companies such as CIGNA and United Health have acquired foreign insurance policies but have yet to establish medical tourism programs (CIGNA, UHC). WellPoint, Inc., a subset of BlueCross BlueShield health insurance, has established a medical tourism pilot program in India (BC/BS). This exemplifies that insurance companies can serve as the mediator to ensure patient quality and ease of return to the United States. American medical centers that extend their facilities abroad also help transfer comprehensive management expertise and intellectual property (Schroth and Khawaja, 2007).

AFFILIATES

Organizations such as the JCI and International Standards Organization (ISO) aid "offshore" facilities in gaining brand recognition with foreign patients. The JCI has become the international standard of healthcare quality assurance. The ISO also accredits institutions based agreed upon international standards of care and hospital-quality management (Herrick, 2007; Milstein & Smith, 2006). American hospitals also have international affiliates that attract both foreign and native patients with their prestigious reputation for care (figure 3.11). The extension of American based hospitals also allows for the transfer and care of patients between the affiliated medical centers. This aids in patient care and treatment upon return to the United States. For example, Memorial Sloan-Kettering's International Center provides a referral service for patients with cancer and who want to arrange an appointment with a Memorial Sloan-Kettering physician, but who are not citizens of the United States or permanent residents of the United States (Memorial Sloan-Kettering).

AMERICAN HOSPITAL	INTERNATIONAL LOCATION	INTERNATIONAL SERVICE
University of Pittsburgh Medical Center	• Developing hospital in Palmero, Italy	Research and education
	• Medical Center in Qatar	
	• Cancer Center in Dublin, Ireland	
Harvard Medicine	Partner with Dubai Healthcare City	Training, medical consulting, infrastructure planning.
Memorial Sloan-Kettering Cancer Center	Relationships with Institutions in China, Spain, Geneva, Greece, San Paulo, Seoul, Istanbul, Singapore and the Philippines	Advisory
Cornell Medical School	• Medical school in Qatar	Research and education
	• Advisory Institute in Seoul	
Duke Medicine	Medical Graduate School in Singapore	Education, training, and research
Johns Hopkins Hospital	Relationships with Institutions in Japan, Singapore, India, UAE, Canada, Lebanon, Turkey, Ireland, Portugal, Chile and Panama City	Research, education, policy planning
Cleveland Clinic	• Partnership with UAE for clinic in Abu Dubai	Education, training, and research
	• Satellite campus in Canada	
Columbia University Medical Center	• Affiliated with Institutions in Paris, Istanbul, and the Philippines	Education, training, research, and consultation
	• Medical School partnership in Israel	

Figure 3.11 United States Hospitals Involved in International Countries

Figure 3.11 shows the United States Hospitals that have international locations and a description of the international services provided (Keckley & Underwood, 2008).

MEDICAL TOURISM

DYNAMIC FIELD

Medical tourism is a new field of medical care that is constantly changing. Despite the fact that medical tourism has been occurring since the 1960s both in-bound and outbound of the United States, it is only recently that we see an explosion of outbound care. Since 2003, medical tourism has become extremely popular and international hospitals have sprung up globally. The dimensions of outbound care, though, are constantly being redefined to include both planning surgery abroad and return care in the United States.

RESEARCH

The numbers, locations, and prices of both in and outmigration of healthcare in the United States is poorly reported and monitored. The booming nature of medical tourism has yielded many to estimate the possibilities of not only the number of people, but the profits achieved by international medical centers. Quality of care research, evidenced based medical outcomes, and clinical protocols need to be monitored for errors and/or adverse events. Currently, there is no global system in place to regulate these measures. In order to completely understand all of the facets of medical tourism more data needs to be collected, so that researchers can begin to understand the impact of medical tourism and what it means for the future of healthcare.

TELEMEDICINE

Medical tourism encompasses telemedicine in that it provides a platform for the exchange of patient information through a global healthcare network. The internet, first and foremost, allows physicians to collaborate from distant locations and offers care to patients in remote locations. The addition of teleconferencing and teleradiology enhances healthcare professionals' ability to communicate, regardless of location, regarding patient's health status. For example, the University of Florida Center for Telehealth uses teleconferencing to provide telehealth consultation (Center for Telehealth and Healthcare Communications). The University of New Mexico uses similar teleconferencing methods to contact patients living in rural areas (University of New Mexico). Internet sites like Telederm use teleconsultation services and the transfer of digital images to give patients advice and feedback on dermatological issues (Telederm.org).

FUTURE IMPLICATIONS

COMBINED/INTERNATIONAL HEALTHCARE SYSTEMS

The success of medical tourism thus far may lead some healthcare providers to reinitiate a combined or even international healthcare system. An international healthcare system was first attempted in the early 1970s by for-profit organizations such as the Hospital Corporation of America and HealthSouth Corporation (Schroth and Khawaja, 2007). The rejuvenation of such a system is evident in United States hospitals, international affiliates. A plan that would incorporate United States and foreign physicians would improve patient care because it would afford the health professionals more communication and medical consultation. Coordinating physicians would generate a team approach to medicine. A combined system also ensures appropriate care upon return to the United States with coordinated physicians. A universal or governmental based health plan may also contract with foreign hospitals for certain elective procedures. This would afford many people, who are currently uninsured, the opportunity to achieve the care they desire at an affordable price.

Many insurance companies, like that of BlueCross BlueShield, offer health insurance options for travelers seeking care outside the United States. This plan allows BlueCross BlueShield card holders to find doctors and hospitals around the world (BC/BS). CIGNA offers an international program for expatriates, in addition to a short-term international health insurance option for employees on assignment abroad (CIGNA).

IMPLICATIONS FOR THE UNITED STATES HEALTHCARE SYSTEM

The outsourcing of healthcare from the United States has and will continue to have a very serious impact on the current healthcare system. As patients move out of the United States for care, health professionals at home are losing revenue. It is estimated that medical tourism in 2006 resulted $15.9 billion dollar revenue loss for United States healthcare providers (Keckley & Underwood, 2008). Nurses, physicians, and other healthcare employees will face a serious job crisis if enough patients migrate out of the United States.

EFFECTS OF GLOBALIZATION OF HEALTH SERVICES AND SYSTEMS

Medical tourism has increased global interaction and ignited a global exchange of knowledge. Patient medical information and procedural techniques are just a few areas where information is being transmitted internationally. The use of telemedicine such as teleconferencing and teleradiology has increased global patient physician interaction and the transfer of sensitive information. The globalization of healthcare networks indicates that quality of care and services has become somewhat equalized across the globe (Schroth and Khawaja, 2007). It is this idea that will drive patients out of the United States and into foreign countries to secure needed healthcare services.

Multinational organizations may employ nurses and physicians to deploy to international locations of the organization to care for American employees abroad. Other professions, such as physical therapists, occupational therapists, and respiratory therapists, could also face the same fate as many large organizations relocate out of the United States and expand existing abroad facilities and contracted health services.

Globalization will also impact native people and local economies in nations that have become medical tourism hot spots. Increased education regarding health and increased access to care are two of the major impacts medical tourism has thus achieved. Public health awareness and the spread of public health services may aid in reviving these "third world" countries. The idea of globalization, and movement of services to "third world" countries, thereby empowers these nations and offers them tremendous economic, academic, and health possibilities.

COMBINED CARE PLANS

Health insurance companies see the monetary savings in sending patients abroad for procedures. Companies like Aetna have even begun offering programs abroad, while others have instituted only aboard surgery options for specific procedures. The results of the BlueCross BlueShield pilot program under WellPoint, Inc. will surely inform other insurance companies of how to handle medical tourism. Insurance companies, though, take risks when offering surgery abroad, including liability and malpractice issues.

Insurance companies may begin offering care options that include domestic and international procedural choices for members. This will allow individual choice based on factors including cost, quality of care, and where they would like to have the procedure performed. An extension of universal healthcare coverage may also offer abroad surgical options to shorten waiting times for elective procedures.

REGULATORY ENVIRONMENT

The institution of standards of care and an officiating environment are critical to the long term success of medical tourism. A regulatory body needs to be instituted to ensure quality of care, ease of access, and appropriate treatment is received by all patients. The regulatory environment should monitor accredited hospitals with data regarding patient care, volume, success rate, and medical outcomes. It should ensure that all international standards are met and that patients are given adequate care. Organizations such as the JCI, WHO, and the WMA have instituted declarations regarding human rights but no single body has been established to enforce these declarations.

LEGAL ISSUES

The legal issues resulting from medical tourism will hopefully be eased by combined care plans and United States extension facilities. Currently, there is not a consistent body of laws that regulates international medical travel and quality of care as new laws are developed and enforced, this will decrease malpractice issues, as the patients can receive coordinated care across multiple countries. International law firms may also flourish due to the increased international patient travel volume and increased likelihood for surgical errors.

INTERNATIONAL SAFETY

Medical tourism poses a variety of international health safety issues. The spread of communicable diseases is made immensely easier by increased travel especially to areas where the disease is prevalent. The Global Health Governance, an initiative of the WHO, aims to apply the legal and customary rules with relation to global health. The Global Health Governance focuses its efforts mainly on promoting and enforcing public health laws (WHO).

World events like 9/11, the kidnapping of wealthy visitors, and the unstable economy may contribute to the international safety. Tragic events and even terrorist attacks can deter visitors by putting their safety at risk. Also, patients may feel unwanted by certain nationalist groups and therefore choose other destinations. The unstable economy of certain medical tourist destinations may also make some patients weary of travel.

SERVICE PERFORMED	WEBSITE	DESCRIPTION
Consultation	http://www.telemedicine.com/	the leveraging of electronic communications to provide medical expertise or treatment to areas where the expertise is not readily available (synchronous or asynchronous)
Radiology	http://www.telradsol.com/	The sending of X-rays, CT scans, or MRIs (store-and-forward images) is the most common application of telemedicine in use today.
Specialty	http://www.telepathology.com/ http://www.telederm.org/	Teledermatology, telepsychiatry, and telepathology
Health	http://www.telehealth.com	patient education and communication solutions for the healthcare market

Figure 3.12 Telemedicine

Figure 3.12 describes the emerging types of telemedicine and a brief description of what each entails.

CONCLUSION

Medical tourism is a new subset of healthcare that is changing the typical method of healthcare delivery. Medical tourism often combines medical treatment with a foreign vacation. Every year thousands of patients leave their homeland and seek treatment abroad. Each patient holds their own reason for traveling, although most outbound tourists are seeking a financial savings. To aid patients in their travel, facilitators such as websites and travel agents have developed programs which incorporate everything from hotel to hospital services. As patients migrate around the globe, international standards need to be implemented and services need to be standardized. Organizations such as JCI and WHO have already instituted standards of care, but international healthcare still lacks a regulatory body. Insurance companies may aid in this process by allowing patients to travel abroad for care. Companies such as Aetna and BlueCross BlueShield have already begun medical tourism programs. The recent increase in telehealth services assists patient-physician communication regardless of location. The future of medical tourism phenomenon is unknown, but if the explosion of outbound patients continues, further investigation is needed to ensure patient safety in the global marketplace.

REFERENCES

BlueCross Blue Shield. (2009). Retrieved November 15, 2009, from http://www.bcbs.com/.

Cigna. (2009). Retrieved November 15, 2009, from http://www.cigna.com/.

Center for Telehealth. (2010). Retrieved on November 15, 2009, from http://telehealth.phhp.ufl.edu/.

Herrick, D. (2007). *Medical Tourism: Global Competition in Healthcare.* (NCPA Policy Report No. 304).

Dallas, Texas: National Center for Policy Analysis.

International Conference on Harmonisation of Technical Requirements for Registration of Pharmaceuticals for Human Use (ICH). (2009). Retrieved November 15, 2009, from http://www.ich.org/cache/compo/276-254-1.html.

International Standards Organizations (ISO). (2009). Retrieved November 15, 2009, from www.iso.org.

Joint Commission International (JCI). (2009). Retrieved November 15, 2009, from
http://www.jointcommissioninternational.org/.

Keckley, P., Underwood, H. (2007). *Medical Tourism: Consumers In Search of Value.*
Washington, DC: Deloitte Center for Health Solutions.

Kelley, E., Hurst, J. (March 2006). Healthcare Quality Indicators ProjectConceptual
Framework Paper. OCED. Retrieved November 15, 2009, from http://www.oecd.
org/dataoe cd/l/36/36262363.pdf.

Memorial Sloan Kettering. (2009). International Patients. Memorial Sloan Kettering.
Retrieved February 1, 2010.

Milstein, A., Smith, M. (2006). America's New Refugees—Seeking Affordable Surgery.

Offshore. *The New England Journal of Medicine*, 355 (16), 1637–1641.

Schroth, L., Khawaja, R (2007). Globalization of Healthcare. *Frontiers of Health
Services Management, 24* (2), 19–30.

Telederm. (2009). Retrieved November 15, 2009, from http://www.telederm.org/
page_dermatology_ home.

Turner, L. (2007). 'First World Healthcare at Third World Prices': Globalization,
Bioethics and Medical Tourism. *Biosocieties, 2,* 303–325.

United Healthcare. (2009). Retrieved November 15, 2009, from http://www.uhc.com/.

University of New Mexico Center for Telehealth and Cybermedicine Research.
(2009). Retrieved on November 15, 2009, from http://hsc.unm.edu/som/
telehealth/index.shtml.

The World Bank. (2009). Data-Country Classification. The World Bank. Retrieved
November 15, 2009, from http://web.worldbank.org/WBSITE/EXTERNAL/
DATASTATIS-TICS/o,,contentMDK:PK:64l33l56~pagePK:64l33l50~piPK:64l33l7
5~theSitePK:239419,00.html.

World Health Organization (WHO). (2009). Retrieved November 15, 2009, from http://www.who.int/en/.

World Medical Association (WMA). (2009). Retrieved November 15, 2009, from http://www.wma.net/en/iohome/index.html.

Alyssa R. Goldbach has been an honor student at Scranton University's College of Arts and Science, who made the Dean's list repeatedly in the past years. She is currently enrolled in the MBA Program at Scranton University, and recently successfully presented on Medical Tourism with Dr. Daniel West at the MBAA International Conference in Chicago, IL. This article is based on Alyssa's research conducted for her graduate research thesis.

Daniel J. West, Jr. is Chairman and Professor at the Department of Health Administration and Human Resources, University of Scranton. He holds a Ph.D., M. Ed., and B.S. from the Pennsylvania State University. He teaches courses in Leadership, Health Care Systems, Medical Practice Administration, and Cultural Diversity. Dr. West practiced healthcare administration for 27 years. He has worked in a variety of settings including hospitals, outpatient clinics, medical group practices, and ambulatory care settings. He also worked with many professional organizations and governmental entities. He enjoys teaching and sharing knowledge in the classroom, and watching graduates make significant contributions to the field. Dr. West is also President/CEO of HTCConsulting Group, a Certified Healthcare Consultant with the American Association of Healthcare Consultants, and is board certified in healthcare management by the American College of Healthcare Executives. He holds several international faculty appointments at universities in other countries.

REFLECTIONS ON THE READING SELECTIONS

We offer the following editorial commentary on the reading selections.

1. Although significant changes to healthcare are occurring in the U.S., the article "A Revolution in Healthcare" identifies how other countries are encountering similar changes with regard to the consumer-driven healthcare marketplace. We encourage you to further examine retail walk-in clinics and the prevalence of urgent care centers and how these are impacting traditional healthcare organizations.

2. In the article by A. Michael LaPenna, he briefly discusses the Cleveland Clinic and the Mayo Clinic. We highly recommend the following two books, which richly discuss why these two prestigious healthcare organizations are so successful:

Berry, Leonard L., and Seltman, Kent D. (2008). *Management lessons from Mayo Clinic: Inside one of the world's most admired service organizations*. New York: McGraw-Hill.

Cosgrove, Toby (2014). *The Cleveland Clinic way: Lessons in excellence from one of the world's leading healthcare organizations*. Ohio: McGraw-Hill.

3. Another comparison of procedural costs in the U.S. and abroad is provided in the article "Medical Tourism: A New Venue of Healthcare." Healthcare organizations in the U.S. need to continually consider the costs of medical procedures and the entire issue of price transparency to consumers. As we move even more toward a consumer-driven model of healthcare, organizations should continue to focus on providing value to the consumer with all of the services they provide to patients and their families.

APPLICATION AND SYNTHESIS

"We need to help get the patient online… it's great to have data, but we need to do something with it and give patients tools that actually manage their health."
—*Robin Wiener, Get Real Health president and founding partner* (EHR Intelligence, 2014)

QUESTIONS FOR DISCUSSION

1. Would you adopt digital healthcare tools? If not, why? If so, what would be the main advantage for you and for your patients?

2. What is your perception of telemedicine? Do you think your perception is different from younger or older physicians?

3. The current top specialties for medical travelers are cosmetic surgery, dentistry, and cardiovascular (angioplasty, CABG, transplants). This industry is growing at

a rate of 15–25% worldwide (http://www.patientsbeyondborders.com/medical-tourism-statistics-facts). What impact do you anticipate medical tourism having on your career?

4. Most medical tourism revolves around procedures that are considered elective for insurance purposes, but Aetna, Blue Cross Blue Shield, and WellPoint are implementing pilot medical tourism programs for covered medical procedures. What impact do you think this will have on the practice of medicine in the U.S. in the future? (http://www.travelchannel.com/interests/wellness-and-renewal/articles/travel-trend-medical-tourism)

5. Some argue it is not "medical tourism" but instead "medical travel." How does changing from tourism to travel impact the concept?

6. What form of alternative healthcare or nontraditional access do you believe is the most valued by patients?

7. What form of alternative healthcare will provide the largest challenge for your organization?

SUMMARY OF MAIN POINTS

After reading this chapter, you should be able to:

√ Discuss what concierge medicine is and how it can be used by physicians (p. 43–47)
√ Identify changes in the healthcare marketplace (p. 48–49)
√ Discuss the rise in medical tourism, telemedicine, and digital health tools (p. 49–52)

COMPREHENSION ASSESSMENT

1. How is concierge medicine different than the traditional physician-patient relationship?

2. What are some of the new and innovative healthcare delivery models?

3. How have HSAs influenced developing consumer healthcare models?

4. What are some of the new relationships between retail and healthcare?

5. Medical tourism covers healthcare into the U.S. and abroad. What are some of the reasons why consumers consider medical tourism as a viable option for their healthcare needs?

CONCLUSION

In this chapter, we discussed the changing competitive landscape for the healthcare market, including the many different healthcare options for consumers. It is important for every healthcare organization to correctly identify all of its competitors, whether traditional competitors such as other physicians and hospitals or less traditional competitors such as emerging healthcare delivery formats. We also discussed digital health tools and how they have revolutionized the way healthcare is delivered to consumers.

The next chapter will focus on the marketing strategy and developing an appropriate marketing plan for your organization.

REFERENCES

American Medical Association (2016). Retrieved from http://www.healthcareitnews. com/blog/doctors-are-growing-digital-health-tools-says-ama http://hitconsultant. net/2016/09/26/digital-health-tools-ama-survey/

Heller, Matthew (2016). *Employers Warm to Telemedicine Benefits*. Retrieved from http://ww2.cfo.com/health-benefits/2016/11/employers-warm-telemedicine-benefits/

HER Intelligence (2014). *Mostashari: Patient engagement is essential for better health*. Retrieved from https://ehrintelligence.com/news/mostashari-patient-engagement-is-essential-for-better-health.

Grace, Maggie (2007). *State of the heart: A medical tourist's true story of lifesaving surgery in India*. Oakland, CA: New Harbinger Publications.

Medical Tourism Association. Retrieved from http://www.medicaltourismassociation. com/en/index.html

Patients Beyond Borders (2016). Medical tourism statistics & facts. Retrieved from http://www.patientsbeyondborders.com/medical-tourism-statistics-facts.

SFU Medical Tourism Research Group (2017). Retrieved from http://medicaltourismandme. com/.

IMAGE CREDITS

4 CHAPTER

STRATEGIC HEALTHCARE MARKETING

LEARNING OBJECTIVES

In this chapter, you will learn about the following:

- The importance of strategic planning
- The steps in strategic planning
- The challenges of strategic planning
- Applying strategic planning to healthcare organizations

INTRODUCTION

One of the most important responsibilities for any marketing department is to provide strategic direction for the healthcare organization. This chapter will help you better understand the steps in the strategic planning process and how to apply strategic marketing decisions in healthcare organizations.

NOTES FROM PRACTICE

Figure 4.1 John Rathnam

"You need to be on dialysis!" was the "death sentence" I received from my nephrologist in August 2008. I wondered how would I cope. Would I die a quick or slow death on dialysis? I was given hope for an evaluation for a transplant, and it would take four months.

However, three-and-a-half years later, I was still being tested. My will to live helped me walk away from the institution. I referred myself to another center because my physician declined to refer me. On March 12, 2013, the fifth scheduled surgery date, I received my kidney transplant. Gratitude overflows for my donor, transplantation professionals, and family and friends who supported me through my journey.

Now the investigation to understand the struggles potential kidney transplant patients face began. Initially, I interviewed transplant coordinators, surgeons, nephrologists, social workers, nurses, dialysis administrators, and patients. The transplant community gave me little hope for improving the current system.

The next step was to obtain the Scientific Registry of Transplant Recipients (SRTR) reports and analyze the results of the 247 transplant centers in the United States. I learned that patient outcomes were very similar, around 90% to 95%. However, there was a vast difference in living and deceased donors at the centers. After identifying the top 25 centers with the highest percentage of living donor transplants, I interviewed many coordinators at these centers. The goal was to identify programs with high living donations. I was surprised! There was not a pattern, nor was there a program to increase living donors. The transplant centers left it up to the patient to find living donors. The word "non-solicitation" was used to avoid educating the patients on the need for living donors. This is the gap I discovered; thus, the "Proactive Education for Family & Friends" program was developed.

To gain credibility in the medical community and acquire knowledge, I completed 64 courses. These include an MBA in healthcare management from the University of Texas at Tyler and certificates from Harvard University, Johns

Hopkins University, Stanford University, University of Florida, etc. in Patient Safety and Improving Healthcare Quality. To understand the kidney transplantation process, I completed a course in Clinical Kidney Transplantation offered by the University of Leiden.

After I was told by the CEO of UNOS that no funds were available from HRSA for increasing living donors, I decided to connect with the transplant community utilizing LinkedIn. Over 6,350 connections are now available by using this powerful marketing tool. We help patients improve their care and journey nationwide. The national task force, which evaluated the program, recommended setting up a 501(c)(3) nonprofit. Courses in marketing and entrepreneurship from the University of Illinois, Duke University, University of North Carolina, and the University of Maryland were helpful in acquiring the knowledge to establish Living Donor Outreach, which received nonprofit status from the IRS on December 29, 2015.

We are marketing the program using social media and personal appeals to transplant centers. Over 70 institutions have received the "Proactive Education for Family & Friends" program, and it is taught live online. We are following up on the results and its utilization. Over 100,000 kidney patients need transplants this year. Our goal is to save lives, just as my life was saved.

John Rathnam is president of Living Donor Outreach, 5130 Acadia Drive, Riverside, CA 92505. He can be reached at jrathnam@earthlink.net or (951)687–7746.

Website: https://livingdonoroutreach.com.

Strategic planning, although a difficult process, is the crux of marketing. However, a strategic plan is only as good as the "buy-in" it receives from top management and employees. Here are some recommendations to improve the "buy-in" process:

1. Engage everyone in the process and the plan

2. Communicate the plan and its goals and importance to employees

3. Manage change and processes to create buy-in

4. Create clear goals and recognize success

5. Build a strong organizational culture to create an atmosphere of trust

He had reduced his business strategy
panic attacks to under three hours.

Figure 4.2 The Challenges of Strategic
Planning in a Changing Environment

READING SELECTION

READING 4.1

DEVELOPING AND ENACTING STRATEGIC MARKETING PLANS

BY JOEL R. EVANS AND BARRY BERMAN

CHAPTER OBJECTIVES

1. To define strategic planning and consider its importance for marketing

2. To describe the total quality approach to strategic planning and show its relevance to marketing

3. To look at the different kinds of strategic plans and the relationships between marketing and the other functional areas in an organization

4. To describe thoroughly each of the steps in the strategic planning process: defining organizational mission, establishing strategic business units, setting marketing objectives, performing situation analysis, developing marketing strategy, implementing tactics, and monitoring results

5. To show how a strategic marketing plan may be devised and applied

IBM (**www.ibm.com**) generates more patents than any other firm. In recent years, the firm has transformed itself from a computer hardware manufacturer to a more diversified company with a major emphasis on its service and software businesses. It is a globally integrated enterprise.

A key to IBM's long-run success is its use of strategic road maps. Here are some highlights of the road map for 2015, as reported at IBM's Web site.

> IBM is an innovation company. We pursue continuous transformation both in what we do and how we do it—always remixing to higher value in our offerings and skills, in our operations and management practices, and in the transformational capabilities we deliver to our clients.

> We continuously change our business mix toward higher-value, more profitable technologies and market opportunities. We have become a globally integrated enterprise to capture new growth and productivity. By aligning our business model with our clients' needs, we achieve our financial goals. This allows us to invest in future sources of growth and provide strong returns to our shareholders. This delivers long-term value and performance for all key IBM stakeholders—investors, clients, employees, and society.

> Five years ago, we saw the emergence of a Smarter Planet (**www.ibm. com/smarterplanet**)—a world becoming instrumented, interconnected, and intelligent. To lead this shift, IBM is pioneering a new computing model—Smarter Computing (**www.ibm.com/smarter-computing**). It has three core attributes: designed for data, defined by software, and open and collaborative. The infusion of digital intelligence into the world's systems is changing the way people, organizations, and entire industries approach what they do.

> Looking ahead, IBM Research (**www.research.ibm.com**) is probing the future of information technology.

Check out the IBM's Smarter Planet Facebook page (**www.facebook.com/
peopleforasmarterplanet**).

In this [reading], we will consider strategic planning from a marketing perspective and review, in depth, each of the steps in the strategic planning.

OVERVIEW

The marketing environment includes a number of factors directed by top management and others directed by marketing. To coordinate these factors and provide guidance for decision making, it is helpful to engage in a formal strategic planning process. For marketers, such a process consists of two key components: a strategic business plan and a strategic marketing plan.

A **strategic business plan** provides "the overall direction an organization will pursue within its chosen environment and guides the allocation of resources and effort. It also provides the logic that integrates the perspectives of functional departments and operating units, and points them all in the same direction." It has (1) an external orientation, (2) a process for formulating strategies, (3) methods for analyzing strategic situations and alternatives, and (4) a commitment to action.[1]

A **strategic marketing plan** outlines the marketing actions to undertake, why they are needed, who is responsible for carrying them out, when and where they will be completed, and how they will be coordinated. A marketing plan is carried out within the context of a firm's broader strategic plan.

Our discussion of strategic planning in marketing is presented early in this book for several reasons. The strategic planning process:

- Gives a firm direction and enables it to better understand the dimensions of marketing research, consumer analysis, and the marketing mix. It is a hierarchical process, moving from company guidelines to specific marketing decisions.
- Makes sure each division's goals are integrated with firmwide goals.
- Encourages different functional areas to coordinate efforts.
- Requires a firm to assess its strengths and weaknesses and to consider environmental opportunities and threats.

- Outlines the alternative actions or combinations of actions a firm can take.
- Presents a basis for allocating resources.
- Highlights the value of assessing performance.

Figure 4.3 highlights how a firm can have a clear and directive strategic vision. Marketing's contribution to strategic planning is a crucial one:

> Marketing plays a vital role in the strategic management process of a firm. The experience of companies well versed in strategic planning indicates that failure in marketing can block the way to goals established by the strategic plan. When the external environment is stable, a company can successfully ride on its technological lead, manufacturing efficiency, and financial acumen. As the environment shifts, however, lack of marketing perspective makes the best-planned strategies treacherous. Indeed, marketing strategy is the most significant challenge that firms of all types and sizes face. As one study noted, "American corporations are beginning to answer a new call to strategic marketing, as many of them shift their business planning priorities more toward strategic marketing and the market planning function."[2]

For example, mass merchandisers such as Wal-Mart (**www.walmart.com**) recognize that each element of their strategy must reflect a customer orientation. Thus, Wal-Mart discount department stores place most floor personnel in product categories where customers want assistance, not evenly throughout stores.

In chapter 4, we discuss a total quality approach to strategic planning, various kinds of strategic plans, relationships between marketing and other functional areas, and the strategic planning process—and show how strategic marketing plans may be outlined and applied.

A general planning Web site (**www.businessplans.org/directory.html**) from Business Resource Software provides good planning materials from a small business perspective.

Textbook Media Press (TMP, **www.textbookmedia.com**) is a Midwest-based publisher that has been publishing affordable textbooks for select courses since 2004. TMP specializes in acquiring the rights to under-served textbooks from the big publishers and revising them for our "textbook media" model. That means a quality textbook from proven authors—a textbook that was developed by the big publishers via peer reviews, and includes ancillaries, but is ***offered to the market at a fraction of the price***.

TMP was founded by a group of former publishing executives and well-known academics looking to deliver a disruptive textbook publishing model. Launched originally as a "freemium" publisher (a front-runner to Flat World Knowledge), and rebranded as Textbook Media in 2009, TMP provides the course instructor with a reliable teaching tool, while offering students a textbook with media options at uniquely affordable prices. TMP's baseline price to students is in the low $20 to $50 range for the E-book version. Other options are E-book/PDF bundle, and an E-book/paperback bundle. Mobile apps and online self-scoring quizzes are also available.

TMP's publishing model is designed for efficiency and speed. The editorial model features renovated properties from proven authors that come with an installed user-base of instructors. Our primary fulfillment model integrates digital publishing and direct delivery. This direct-to-student model with digital delivery is an efficient fulfillment process that reduces manufacturing costs and returns, while eliminating inventory. (Note: TMP does fulfill bookstore orders as requested.) By combining these attributes, TMP is uniquely positioned to succeed in an industry where high-priced products with packaging gimmicks are under attack, and where course instructors are seeking alternatives. The TMP publishing model has been honed over ten years in the market, servicing hundreds of instructor users, and delivering affordable textbooks to over a million college students since our inception.

Figure 4.3 The Clear Strategic Vision of Textbook Media Press
Source: Reprinted by permission.

A TOTAL QUALITY APPROACH TO STRATEGIC PLANNING

Any firm—small or large, domestic or global, manufacturing- or services-driven—should adopt a total quality viewpoint when devising a strategic plan. **Total quality** is a process- and output-related philosophy, whereby a firm strives to fully satisfy customers in an effective and efficient manner. To flourish, a total quality program needs a customer focus, top management commitment, an emphasis on continuous improvement, and support from employees, suppliers, and distribution intermediaries:

- *Process-related philosophy*—Total quality is based on all the activities that create, develop, market, and deliver a good or service for the customer. A company gains a competitive advantage if it offers better-quality goods and services than competitors or if it offers the same quality at a lower price.
- *Output-related philosophy*—Although process-related activities give a good or service its value, the consumer usually can only judge the total quality of the finished product that he or she purchases. Many consumers care about what they buy, rather than how it was made.
- *Customer satisfaction*—To the consumer, total quality refers to how well a good or service performs. Customer service is a key element in a person's ultimate satisfaction, which is affected by the gap between that person's expectations of product performance and actual performance.
- *Effectiveness*—To a marketer, this involves how well various marketing activities (such as adding new product features) are received by consumers.
- *Efficiency*—To a marketer, this involves the costs of various marketing activities. A firm is efficient when it holds down costs, while offering consumers the appropriate level of quality.
- *Customer focus*—With a total quality viewpoint, a firm perceives the consumer as a partner and seeks input from that partner as it creates, develops, markets, and delivers a good or service.
- *Top management commitment*—Senior executives must be dedicated to making a total quality program work and to ensuring that corners are not cut in an attempt to be more efficient. In the best firms, "total quality" becomes ingrained as part of the corporate culture.
- *Continuous improvement*—A firm must continuously improve its quality because, in most cases, today's total quality will become tomorrow's suboptimal quality. A complacent company will be hurt by the dynamics of the marketplace and fast-paced technological and global marketplace trends.

- *Employee support and involvement*—Employees must "buy into" a total quality program for it to work. Empowering employees not only gets them involved in the total quality process, but it also assures that customer problems are promptly addressed and resolved in the customer's favor.
- *Supplier and distributor support and involvement*—Suppliers and resellers can greatly affect total quality due to their involvement in creating it. They too must "buy into" a firm's total quality efforts.

Figure 4.4 shows how a total quality program should work. At the left are the participants who create total quality. There is an interchange among the parties and between the parties and the process. In this way, a good's or service's effectiveness and efficiency are influenced. Total quality is the output. The process and total quality itself are regularly improved. If a consumer feels a product has superior total quality, a purchase is made. When experience with a purchase is pleasing, customer satisfaction occurs. Because one measure of effectiveness is customer satisfaction, there is an impact arrow.

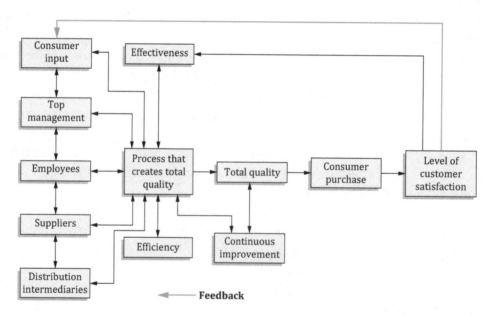

Figure 4.4 The Keys to a Successful Total Quality Program

Satisfaction is feedback that places consumer input into the process. The consumer's central focus is evident because this party appears three times: consumer input, consumer purchase, and customer satisfaction. At the Ritz-Carlton hotel chain (**www.ritzcarlton.com**), the only hotel company to twice win the Malcolm Baldrige National Quality award, total quality is imperative: "The Ritz-Carlton is a place where the genuine care and comfort of our guests is our highest mission. We pledge to provide the finest personal service and facilities for our guests who will always enjoy a warm, relaxed, yet refined ambience. The Ritz-Carlton experience enlivens the senses, instills well-being, and fulfills even the unexpressed wishes and needs of our guests. At Ritz-Carlton, 'We are Ladies and Gentlemen serving Ladies and Gentlemen.' Our Ladies and Gentlemen are the most important resource in our service commitment to our guests. By applying the principles of trust, honesty, respect, integrity, and commitment, we nurture and maximize talent to the benefit of each individual and the company."[3]

DIGITAL MARKETING IN PRACTICE

The reputation of any firm is greatly impacted by the total quality expectations of that firm and other parties—including consumers, suppliers, and distribution intermediaries. If there is a breakdown or disconnect, the firm will suffer, especially in the era of intense social media attention. Take a look at "Online Reputation Management" (**http://wp.me/p2qANL-1kt**) to learn about how to better manage one's reputation.

Sometimes, the total quality process breaks down in a way that may be difficult to fix. For example, many firms have had glitches with their Web sites, including heavy traffic causing system overloads, poor inventory and shipping coordination, too long a time for replies to E-mail, and so forth. These problems require expensive and time-consuming solutions. To learn more about the strategic aspects of total quality management (TQM), visit the Bain & Company TQM Web site (**http://t.co/nlZfi-AWKEp**). It highlights the role of marketing in TQM.

Strategic plans can be categorized by their duration, scope, and method of development. They range from short run, specific, and department generated to long run, broad, and management generated.

Plans may be short run (typically 1 year), moderate in length (2 to 5 years), or long-run (5 to 10 or even 15 years). Many firms rely on a combination: Short-run and moderate-length plans are more detailed and operational in nature than long-run plans.

Japan's Canon (**http://www.canon.com**), the maker of cameras, machines, and optical products, has taken this planning approach:

(1) We believe sound growth is predicated on strengthening our primary businesses. With innovative and attractive industry-leading products, and an emphasis on highly profitable solutions and services, we aim to achieve the overwhelming No. 1 position in each of our primary businesses. At the same time, we continue to grow secondary businesses in related areas, such as network cameras and the retail photo segment. (2) To date, we had made Japan the center for innovation. Now, however, we are looking to mergers and acquisitions and other methods to achieve innovation in the U.S. and Europe as well, creating a global R&D framework based on our Three Regional Headquarters management system. (3) Canon optimizes productivity by diversifying production facilities worldwide. We comprehensively assess such factors as distribution, parts procurement, labor, and risk. Production is further enhanced through the in-house production of tools, materials, and technologies. (4) As developing and resource-rich economies in Asia, South America, and Africa join the ranks of the world's growth centers, Canon continuously assesses trends and aligns our global sales structure accordingly. In Europe and the U.S., for instance, we are strengthening our services and solutions sales force. In Asia, we focus on the Chinese market while expanding sales in ASEAN countries. (5) Our enterprising spirit has enabled us to continuously transform the company over many decades. This is reflected in Canon's guiding principles—the San-ji (Three Selfs) Spirit—which have been passed down since the company's founding. Today, we actively work to maintain a corporate culture that values transformation. At the same time, our training programs help to develop personnel befitting a truly excellent global company.[4]

The scope of strategic plans also varies. There may be separate marketing plans for each of a firm's major products, a single integrated marketing plan encompassing all products, or a broad business plan with a section devoted to marketing. Separate marketing plans by product line are often used by consumer-goods manufacturers, a single integrated marketing plan is often employed by service firms, and a broad business plan is often utilized by industrial-goods manufacturers. A firm's diversity and the number of distinct market segments it seeks both have a strong influence.

Last, plans may be devised by a bottom-up, top-down, or combination approach. In bottom-up planning, input from salespeople, product managers, advertising people, and other marketing areas is used to set goals, budgets, forecasts, timetables, and marketing mixes. Bottom-up plans are realistic and good for morale. Yet, it may be hard to coordinate bottom-up plans and to include different assumptions about the same concept when integrating a company-wide plan. Shortcomings of bottom-up plans are resolved in the top-down approach, whereby senior managers centrally direct planning. A top-down plan can use complex assumptions about competition or other external factors and provide a uniform direction for marketing. Input from lower-level managers is not actively sought, and morale may diminish. A combination of the two approaches could be used if senior executives set overall goals and policy, and marketing personnel form plans for carrying out marketing activities.

STRENGTHENING RELATIONSHIPS BETWEEN MARKETING AND OTHER FUNCTIONAL AREAS IN AN ORGANIZATION

An organization's strategic planning efforts must accommodate the distinct needs of marketing and other functional areas. This is not always simple, due to the different orientations of each area, as shown in table 4.1. Marketers may seek tailor-made products, flexible budgets, nonroutine transactions, many product versions, frequent purchases, customer-driven new products, employee compensation incentives, and aggressive actions against competitors. This may conflict with goals of other functional areas to seek mass production (production), stable budgets (finance), routine transactions (accounting), limited models (engineering), infrequent orders (purchasing), technology-driven new products (research and development), fixed employee compensation (personnel), and passive actions against competitors (legal).

TABLE 4.1 THE ORIENTATIONS OF DIFFERENT FUNCTIONAL AREAS

FUNCTIONAL AREA	MAJOR STRATEGIC ORIENTATION
Marketing	To attract and retain a loyal group of consumers through a unique combination of product, distribution, promotion, and price factors
Production	To utilize full plant capacity, hold down per-unit production costs, and maximize quality control
Finance	To operate within established budgets, focus on profitable items, control customer credit, and minimize loan costs for the company
Accounting	To standardize reports, detail costs fully, and routinize transactions
Engineering	To develop and adhere to exact product specifications, limit models and options, and concentrate on quality improvements
Purchasing	To acquire items via large, uniform orders at low prices and maintain low inventories
Research and Development	To seek technological breakthroughs, improvements in product quality, and recognition for innovations
Personnel	To hire, motivate, supervise, and compensate employees in an efficient manner
Legal	To ensure that a strategy is defensible against challenges from the government, competitors, channel members, and consumers

Top management's job is to ensure that every functional area sees the need for a balanced view in company decision making and has input on decisions. Although a degree of tension among departments is inevitable, conflict can be reduced by encouraging inter-functional contact; seeking personnel with both technical and marketing expertise; forming multifunctional task forces, committees, and management-development programs; and setting goals for each department that take other departments into account.

THE STRATEGIC PLANNING PROCESS

The **strategic planning process** has seven interrelated steps: defining organizational mission, establishing strategic business units, setting marketing objectives, performing situation analysis, developing marketing strategy, implementing tactics, and monitoring results. Because the process encompasses both strategic business planning and strategic marketing planning, it should be conducted by a combination of senior company executives and marketers. The strategic planning process is depicted in figure 4.5.

This process applies to small and large firms, consumer and industrial firms, goods-and services-based firms, domestic and global firms, and profit-oriented and nonprofit-oriented institutions. Planning at each step in the process may differ by type of firm, but using a thorough strategic plan is worthwhile for any company. Sample plans for three businesses—manufacturer, service provider, and retailer—are available at the Business Owner's Toolkit site (**www.toolkit.com/tools/bt.aspx?tid=buspln_m**).

The steps in strategic planning are discussed in the following sections.

DEFINING ORGANIZATIONAL MISSION

Organizational mission refers to a long-term commitment to a type of business and a place in the market. It "describes the scope of the firm and its dominant emphasis and values," based on that firm's history, current management preferences, resources, and distinctive competences, and on environmental factors.[5]

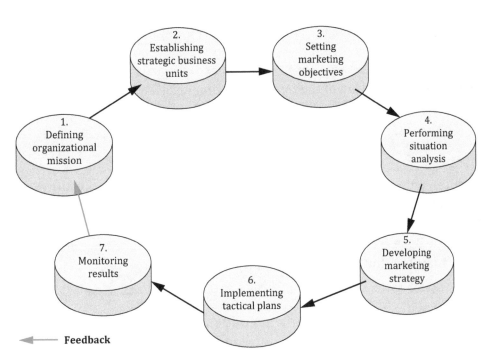

Figure 4.5 The Strategic Planning Process

An organizational mission can be expressed in terms of the customer group(s) served, the goods and services offered, the functions performed, and/or the technologies utilized. It is more comprehensive than the line-of-business concept noted in chapter 2. Organizations that diversify too much may not have a clear sense of direction. The mission is considered implicitly whenever a firm:

- Seeks a new customer group or abandons an existing one,
- Introduces a new product (good or service) category or deletes an old one, acquires another company, or sells a business,
- Engages in more marketing functions (a wholesaler opening retail stores) or in fewer marketing functions (a small innovative toy maker licensing its inventions to an outside company that produces, distributes, and promotes them), or
- Shifts its technological focus (a phone manufacturer placing more emphasis on cellular phones).

Why is a clear organizational mission so important? Consider these observations from the RPPC (**www.rppc.net**) consulting group: "Every organization needs to define its fundamental purpose, philosophy, and values. The mission statement answers the basic question of why the organization exists and tells the purpose of the business." It "helps clarify what business you are in, as well as your goals and objectives. It should clearly convey the direction of the business or organization."[6]

ETHICS AND SOCIAL RESPONSIBILITY IN PRACTICE

As a rule, companies can no longer afford to ignore social responsibility issues or to keep quiet about their efforts in being more socially responsible. These efforts need to be incorporated right into the strategic planning process. See how this can be done by reading "Building More Socially Responsible Corporations" **http://t.co/TSXNmyz9x7**

Here is an illustration of a clear organizational mission:

At Southwest Airlines (**www.southwest.com**), our mission statement has always governed the way we do business. It highlights our desire to serve customers and gives us direction when we have to make service-related decisions. It is a way of saying, "we always try to do the right thing!" Foremost, we want you to know that it is *never* our wish to inconvenience our valued customers. We tell employees we are in the customer service business—we just happen to provide air transportation. Our employees understand our mission and we are happy to share it with you, our valued customer. Our customer service commitment was designed and written in such a way as to clarify many of the most commonly questioned terms and conditions of our air travel and provide you with insight into policies and procedures. Southwest is proud to incorporate its customer service commitment in its official contract of carriage reinforcing our pledge to provide safe, affordable, reliable, timely, courteous, and efficient air transportation and baggage handling on every flight, as well as produce a fair return on our shareholders' investments.[7]

ESTABLISHING STRATEGIC BUSINESS UNITS

After defining its mission, a firm may form strategic business units. Each **strategic business unit (SBU)** is a self-contained division, product line, or product department in an organization with a specific market focus and a manager with complete responsibility for integrating all functions into a strategy. An SBU may include all products with the same physical features or products bought for the same use by customers, depending on the mission of the organization. Each SBU has these general attributes:

- A specific target market
- Its own senior marketing executive
- Control over its resources
- Its own marketing strategy
- Clear-cut competitors
- Distinct differential advantages

The SBU concept lets firms identify the business units with the most earnings potential and allocate to them the resources needed for growth. For instance, at General Electric, every SBU must have a unique purpose, identifiable competitors, and all its major business functions (manufacturing, finance, and marketing) within control of that SBU's manager. Units not performing up to expectations are constantly reviewed and, if needed, consolidated with other units, sold, or closed down.

The number of SBUs depends on a firm's organizational mission and resources, and the willingness of top management to delegate authority. A small or specialized firm can have as few as one SBU; a diversified firm can have up to 100 or more. The rather specialized WD-40 Company (**www.wd40.com**) has three main SBUs: multipurpose lubricants (WD-40 and 3-in-One), heavy-duty hand cleaners (Lava and Solvol), and household products (such as Carpet Fresh, Spot Shot, and 2000 Flushes). And the highly diversified Johnson & Johnson (**www.jnj.com**), with 250+ SBUs, is "the world's sixth-largest consumer health company, the world's largest and most diverse medical devices and diagnostics company, the world's fifth-largest biologics company, and the world's eighth-largest pharmaceuticals company."[8]

Firms sometimes eliminate SBUs that do not fit for them. A while back, after careful consideration, PepsiCo (**www.pepsico.com**) spun off its restaurant SBUs—KFC, Pizza Hut, and Taco Bell—to concentrate on three businesses: carbonated beverages, snack foods, and noncarbonated beverages. PepsiCo then acquired Quaker Oats, with its Gatorade drinks and other food products.

SETTING MARKETING OBJECTIVES

A firm needs overall marketing objectives, as well as goals for each SBU. Objectives are often described in both quantitative terms (dollar sales, percentage profit growth, market share, etc.) and qualitative terms (image, level of innovativeness, industry leadership role, etc.).

For example, Hewlett-Packard (HP, **www.hp.com**) is a 75-year-old technology company that is in the midst of a reinvention of itself. As CEO Meg Whitman recently stated: "Success hinges on consistency of leadership, focus, execution, and most importantly, great products and services. We are in a multiyear journey to turn HP around, and we have put in place a plan to restore HP to growth. We know where we need to go, and we're making progress. We continue to drive product innovation in our core markets, with a focus on cloud, security, and big data. We see big opportunities ahead, and we are well positioned to take advantage of these opportunities with our remarkable set of assets and strengths."[9] Here are HP's corporate objectives:

> **Customer loyalty**—We earn customer respect and loyalty by consistently providing the highest quality and value.

Profit—We achieve sufficient profit to finance growth, create value for our shareholders, and achieve our corporate objectives.

Growth—We recognize and seize opportunities for growth that build upon our strengths and competencies.

Market leadership—We lead in the marketplace by developing and delivering useful and innovative products, services, and solutions.

Commitment to employees—We demonstrate our commitment to employees by promoting and rewarding based on performance and by creating a work environment that reflects our values.

Leadership capability—We develop leaders at all levels who achieve business results, exemplify our values, and lead us to grow and win.

Global citizenship—We fulfill our responsibility to society by being an economic, intellectual, and social asset to each country and community where we do business.[10]

Small firms' goals may be less ambitious than those set by their larger counterparts, but they are no less important. Goals are necessary to focus the firm and allow it to monitor the level of success or failure. Without goals, how can a firm really measure its performance?

PERFORMING SITUATION ANALYSIS

In **situation analysis**, also known as SWOT analysis, an organization identifies its internal strengths (S) and weaknesses (W), as well as external opportunities (O) and threats (T). Situation analysis seeks to answer: Where is a firm now? Where is it headed? Answers are derived by recognizing both company strengths and weaknesses relative to competitors, studying the environment for opportunities and threats, assessing the firm's ability to capitalize on opportunities and to minimize or avoid threats, and anticipating competitors' responses to company strategies. The Business Owner's Toolkit site (**http://t.co/Oi3jhc3a3P**) provides an in-depth discussion of many of the factors to be reviewed during a situation analysis.

Situation analysis can, and should, be conducted at any point in a firm's life. Consider this example, as reported by *MarketLine*:

Procter & Gamble (P&G, **www.pg.com**) holds leading global market shares in a variety of product categories. The company's blades and razors category holds a 70 percent global market share, and oral care category holds a number two market share position with over 20 percent of the market. The feminine care category has a more than 30 percent global market share, baby care category has a nearly 35 percent market share, fabric care has 25 percent, home care 15 percent, and the batteries category over 25 percent.

Strengths—Leading market position via a strong brand portfolio, significant R&D and marketing investments, strategic acquisitions that expanded P&G's product portfolio, increasing presence in developing markets, robust cash productivity.

Weaknesses—Increasing instances of product recalls.

Opportunities—Growing men's grooming industry, possibilities to improve productivity, growing personal care and home care markets.

Threats—Rising input cost inflation, counterfeit goods.[11]

Here's what a small new consulting firm's SWOT analysis might look like: *Strengths*—"We are able to respond quickly as we have no red tape and no need for higher management approval. We can give really good customer care, as our current small amount of work means we have a lot of time to devote to customers. Our lead consultant has a strong reputation. We have low overhead." *Weaknesses*—"Our firm has no market presence. We have a small staff with limited skills in some areas. We are vulnerable to vital staff becoming sick or leaving. Our cash flow will be erratic in the early stages." *Opportunities*—"Our business sector is expanding, with many future possibilities for success. Our local chamber of commerce recommends local businesses for work where possible. Competitors may be slow to adopt new technologies." *Threats*—"Will developments in technology affect this market beyond our ability to adapt? A small change in focus of a large competitor might wipe out any market position we achieve."[12]

Situation analysis may sometimes reveal weaknesses or threats that cannot be overcome, and a firm drops or sells a product line or division. In the mid-1990s, General Mills (**www.generalmills.com**) sold its popular restaurant division—comprised of the Red Lobster, Olive Garden, and China Coast chains. Why? Fifty-five percent of General Mills' food profits were used to fund the restaurant business, and the firm decided to focus instead on its leading food brands. This is the focus today: "General Mills gets its Kix vying for the top spot among cereal makers. Every year, it jockeys with Kellogg (**www.kellogg.com**) to be number one in that market with a brand arsenal that includes kid-friendly Kix, as well as Chex, Cheerios, Lucky Charms, and Wheaties. Not just a cereal maker, General Mills is actually one of the largest food companies in the world. Some of its number one and number two market-leading brands are Betty Crocker dessert mixes, Gold Medal flour, Green Giant vegetables, Pillsbury cookie dough, and Yoplait yogurt. Although most of its sales come from the United States, General Mills is trying to grow the reach and position of its brands around the world."[13]

Figure 4.6 shows what may happen without a realistic, proactive, and ongoing SWOT analysis.

DEVELOPING MARKETING STRATEGY

A **marketing strategy** outlines the way in which the marketing mix is used to attract and satisfy the target market(s) and achieve an organization's goals. Marketing-mix decisions center on product, distribution, promotion, and price plans. A separate strategy is necessary for each SBU in an organization; these strategies must be coordinated.

A marketing strategy should be clear to provide proper guidance. It should take into account a firm's mission, resources, abilities, and standing in the marketplace; the status of the firm's industry and the product groups in it (such as laptop PCs versus all-in-one printers); domestic and global competition; such environmental factors as the economy and population trends; and the best growth options—and the threats that could dampen its prospects. For instance, McDonald's (**www.mcdonalds.com**) does a lot of image advertising as part of its overall marketing strategy to enhance its stature in the business community.

Four strategic planning approaches are presented next: product/market opportunity matrix, Boston Consulting Group matrix, General Electric business screen, and Porter generic strategy model.

"Even though I started my company 10 years ago, I still consider it a start-up. Because it hasn't made a dime and not a soul knows we exist."

Figure 4.6 SWOT Analysis: Too Little, Too Late

THE PRODUCT/MARKET OPPORTUNITY MATRIX

The **product/market opportunity matrix** identifies four alternative marketing strategies to maintain and/or increase sales of business units and products: market penetration, market development, product development, and diversification.[14] See figure 4.7. The choice of an alternative depends on the market saturation of an SBU or product and the firm's ability to introduce new products. Two or more alternatives may be combined.

Market penetration is effective when the market is growing or not yet saturated. A firm seeks to expand the sales of its present products in its present markets through more intensive distribution, aggressive promotion, and competitive pricing. Sales are increased by attracting nonusers and competitors' customers and raising the usage rate among current customers.

Market development is effective when a local or regional business looks to widen its market, new market segments are emerging due to changes in consumer lifestyles and demographics, and innovative uses are discovered for a mature product. A firm seeks greater sales of present products from new markets or new product uses. It can enter new territories, appeal to segments it is not yet satisfying, and reposition existing items. New distribution methods may be tried; promotion efforts are more descriptive.

Product development is effective when an SBU has a core of strong brands and a sizable consumer following. A firm develops new or modified products to appeal to present markets. It stresses new models, better quality, and other minor innovations closely related to entrenched products—and markets them to loyal customers. Traditional distribution methods are used; promotion stresses that the new product is made by a well-established firm.

Diversification is used so a firm does not become too dependent on one SBU or product line. The firm becomes involved with new products aimed at new markets. These products may be new to the industry or new only to the company. Both distribution and promotion orientations are different from those usually followed by the firm.

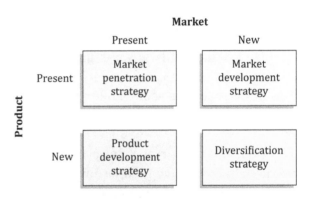

Figure 4.7 The Product/Market Opportunity Matrix

Source: Adapted from H. Igor Ansoff, "Strategies for Diversification," *Harvard Business Review*, Vol. 35 (September-October 1957), pp. 113–124.

Here is how the product/market opportunity matrix can be applied to United Parcel Service—UPS (**www.ups.com**):

- Market penetration—UPS is the world's largest package-delivery firm. It advertises extensively on TV, online, and in magazines. The latest slogan is "We ♥ Logistics." Annually, UPS handles more than 4 billion packages for 9 million customers.

- Market development—It is stepping up efforts around the world, where client use of delivery services tends to be much less than in the United States. In 1990, UPS International operated in 40 nations; now, it operates in more than 220 countries and territories. The firm's Web site is accessible in 25 languages and dialects, and has dedicated content in most of the countries it serves.
- Product development—UPS now offers more shipping choices than ever before, including Express Critical, Next Day Air Early A.M., Next Day Air, Next Day Air Saver, 2nd Day Air A.M., 2nd Day Air, 3 Day Select, Ground, Hundredweight Service, and various Worldwide Express services.
- Diversification—Though the major focus of UPS is package delivery, it has such subsidiaries as UPS Supply Chain Solutions (**www.ups-scs.com**)—offering supply chain support, from transportation to customs; UPS Capital (**www. upscapital.com**)—a provider of financial and insurance solutions; UPS Customized Solutions (**www.ups-psi.com**)—a global management consulting group that delivers business solutions; and the UPS Store (**www.theupsstore.com**), which operates about 4,800 stores.[15]

THE BOSTON CONSULTING GROUP MATRIX

The **Boston Consulting Group matrix** lets a firm classify each SBU in terms of market share relative to key competitors and annual industry growth. A firm can see which SBUs are dominant compared to competitors and whether the industries in which it operates are growing, stable, or declining. The matrix comprises stars, cash cows, question marks, and dogs, as well as the strategies for them.[16] See figure 4.8.

The presumption is that the higher an SBU's market share, the better its long-run marketplace status because of lower per-unit costs and higher profitability (**www. bcg.com**).

This is due to economies of scale (large firms can automate or standardize production, service tasks, distribution, promotion, and so on), experience (as operations are repeated, a firm becomes more effective), and better bargaining power. At the same time, the industry growth rate indicates a firm's need to invest. A high growth rate means a substantial investment will be needed to maintain or expand the firm's position in a growing market.

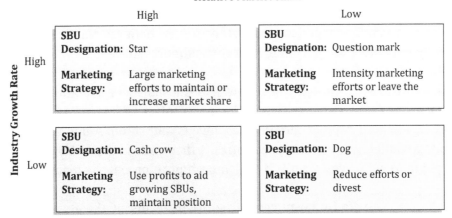

Relative market share is an SBU's market share in comparison to the leading competitors in the industry, industry growth rate is the annual growth of all similar businesses in the market (such as sugarless gum).

Figure 4.8 The Boston Consulting Group Matrix
Source: Adapted from Bruce D. Henderson, "The Experience Curve Reviewed: IV. The Growth Share Matrix of the Product Portfolio" (Boston: Boston Consulting Group, 1973). *Perspectives*, No. 135.

A *star* is a leading SBU (high market share) in an expanding industry (high growth). The main goal is to sustain differential advantages despite rising competition. It can generate substantial profits but needs financing to grow. Market share can be kept or increased by intensive advertising, product introductions, greater distribution, and/ or price reductions. As industry growth slows, a star becomes a cash cow.

A *cash cow* is a leading SBU (high market share) in a mature or declining industry (low growth). It often has loyal customers, making it tough for competitors. Because sales are steady, without high costs for product development and the like, a cash cow yields more cash (profit) than needed to hold its market share. Profits support the growth of other company SBUs. Marketing is oriented to reminder ads, periodic discounts, keeping up distribution channels, and offering new styles or options to encourage repurchases.

A *question mark* is an SBU that has had little impact (low market share) in an expanding industry (high growth). There is low consumer support, differential advantages are weak, and competitors are leaders. To improve, a big marketing investment is needed in the face of strong competition. A firm must decide whether to beef up promotion, add distributors, improve product attributes, and cut prices—or to abandon the market. The choice depends on whether a firm believes the SBU can compete successfully with more support and what that support will cost.

A *dog* is an SBU with limited sales (low market share) in a mature or declining industry (low growth). Despite time in the marketplace, it has little customer interest—and lags behind competitors in sales, image, and so on. A dog usually has cost disadvantages and few growth opportunities. A firm with such an SBU can appeal to a specialized market, harvest profits by cutting support, or exit the market.

Let's look at Microsoft (**www.microsoft.com**) in terms of the Boston Consulting Group matrix. Unfortunately for Microsoft, it currently has no products that could be deemed as stars—with a high market share in a high-growth industry sector. It keeps trying for stars, but has not really succeeded in this category in recent years. Microsoft does have multiple cash cows—with a high market share in a mature industry sector. Its products in this category include its Office suite of software, Xbox game players, and Windows operating systems. Microsoft's major question marks—with a low market share in a high-growth industry sector—are its Skype business (whereby people can call, see, message, and share with others) and the Surface tablet. Skype is placed in this category because it has not achieved significant market share in the pay-per-call market, even though it is a very popular free service. Despite Microsoft's heavy investment in the Bing search engine, Bing can be termed a dog because its search engine market share remains low, and the growth of this industry sector has slowed.[17]

THE GENERAL ELECTRIC BUSINESS SCREEN

The **General Electric business screen** categorizes SBUs and products in terms of industry attractiveness and company business strengths. It uses more variables than either the product/market opportunity matrix or the Boston Consulting Group matrix. Industry attractiveness is based on market size and growth, competition, technological advances, and the social/legal environment. Company business strengths encompass differential advantages, market share, patent protection, marketing effectiveness, control over prices, and economies of scale. An SBU may have high, medium, or low industry attractiveness, as well as high, medium, or low business strengths; it would be positioned accordingly on the business screen in figure 4.9.[18]

SBUs in green are investment/growth areas. They are in strong industries and performing well. They are similar to stars in the Boston Consulting Group matrix. Full marketing resources are proper, and high profits are expected. Innovations, product-line extensions, product and image ads, distribution intensity, and solid price margins are pursued.

SBUs in yellow are selectivity/earnings areas. They are not positioned as well as investment/growth SBUs. An SBU may be strong in a weak industry (as a cash cow), okay in a somewhat attractive industry, or weak in an attractive industry (as a question mark).

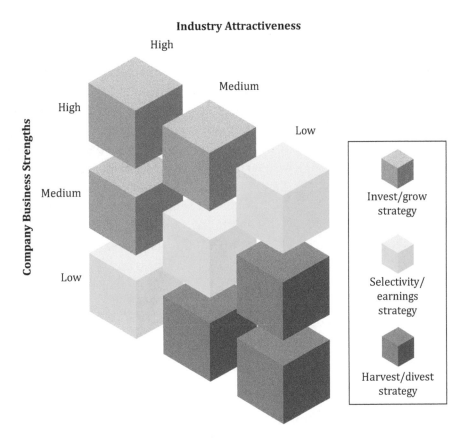

Figure 4.9 The General Electric Business Screen
Source: Adapted from *Maintaining Strategies for the Future through Current Crises* (Fairfield, CT: General Electric, 1975).

A firm wants to hold the earnings and strength of cash cows, and use marketing to maintain customer loyalty and distribution support. For question marks, a firm must decide whether to raise its marketing investment, focus on a specialized market niche, acquire another business in the industry, or trim product lines. The medium/medium SBU is an opportunity to appeal to underserved segments and invest selectively in marketing.

SBUs in red represent harvest/divest areas. They are similar to dogs in the Boston Consulting Group matrix. A firm can minimize its marketing effort, concentrate on a few products rather than a product line, divest, or close down the SBU. Profits are harvested because investments are minimal.

Bausch & Lomb (**www.bausch.com**) applies the fundamentals of the business screen. Now a division of Valeant Pharmaceuticals, "Bausch & Lomb is solely dedicated to protecting and enhancing the gift of sight for millions of people around the world—from the moment of birth through every phase of life. Our mission is simple yet powerful: Helping you see better to live better." Bausch & Lomb offers "the widest and finest range of eye health products, including contact lenses and lens care products, pharmaceuticals, intra-ocular lenses, and other eye surgery products. By listening to our customers and patients, by constantly honing our innovation edge, by executing with integrity and excellence, we strive to earn the trust of our partners and stakeholders. Over the last 160 years, we have become a global hallmark for innovation and quality. Our talented and motivated colleagues work relentlessly to invent new materials, engineer new technologies, and ultimately bring new innovations to help people see better to live better."[19] To concentrate on its main businesses, Bausch & Lomb sold its sunglass SBU (featuring Ray-Ban), its Miracle Ear hearing aid SBU, and its animal research SBU.

Visit the GE Global Research Blog (**http://ge.geglobalresearch.com/blog**) to read about GE's expectations about the future of technology from the firm that has given us the GE business screen.

THE PORTER GENERIC STRATEGY MODEL

The **Porter generic strategy model** identifies two key marketing planning concepts and the options available for each: competitive scope (broad or narrow target) and competitive advantage (lower cost or differentiation). The model pinpoints these basic strategies: cost leadership, differentiation, and focus.[20] See figure 4.10.

With a *cost leadership strategy*, an SBU aims at a broad target market and offers goods or services in large quantities. Due to economies of scale, a firm can reduce per-unit costs and have low prices. This gives it higher profit margins than competitors, allows better responses to cost increases, and/or lures price-conscious consumers. Among those using cost leadership are UPS (**www.ups.com**), DuPont (**www.dupont.com**), and Wal-Mart (**www.walmart.com**).

In a *differentiation strategy*, an SBU aims at a large market by offering goods or services viewed as quite distinctive. The goods or services have a broad appeal, yet are perceived by consumers as unique by virtue of features, availability, reliability, and so on; price is less important. Among those using differentiation are Federal Express (**www.fedex.com**), Seiko (**www.seikowatches.com**), and Caterpillar Tractor (**www.cat.com**).

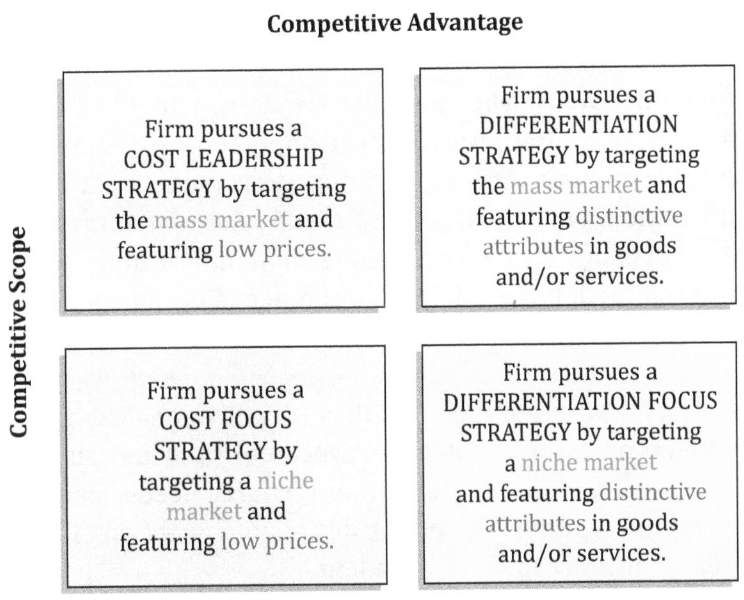

Competitive Advantage

Firm pursues a COST LEADERSHIP STRATEGY by targeting the mass market and featuring low prices.	Firm pursues a DIFFERENTIATION STRATEGY by targeting the mass market and featuring distinctive attributes in goods and/or services.
Firm pursues a COST FOCUS STRATEGY by targeting a niche market and featuring low prices.	Firm pursues a DIFFERENTIATION FOCUS STRATEGY by targeting a niche market and featuring distinctive attributes in goods and/or services.

(Competitive Scope — vertical axis label)

Figure 4.10 The Porter Generic Strategy Model
Source: Developed by the authors based on concepts in Michael E. Porter, *Competitive Advantage: Creating and Sustaining Superior Performance* (New York: Free Press, 1985), pp. 11–16.

With a *focus strategy*, an SBU (which could be a small firm) seeks a narrow market segment via low prices or a unique offering. It can control costs by concentrating on a few key products aimed at specific consumers (cost focus) or by having a specialist reputation and serving a market unsatisfied by competitors (differentiation focus). Printek Direct! (**www.printekdirect.com**) markets refurbished printers to cost-conscious customers, while the Baby Jogger Company (**www.babyjogger.com**) makes a line of strollers for those who like jogging with their babies and toddlers. A neighborhood hardware store usually has a good combination of service, convenient location, and long hours; a local radio station may cater to an over-50 audience by playing mostly rock music from the 1960s, 1970s, and 1980s.

The Porter model shows that a small firm can profit by concentrating on one competitive niche, even though its total market share may be low. A firm does not have to be large to do well.

EVALUATION OF STRATEGIC PLANNING APPROACHES

The strategic planning approaches just discussed are widely used—at least informally. Many firms assess alternative market opportunities; know which products are stars, cash cows, question marks, and dogs; recognize what factors affect performance; understand their industries; and realize they can target broad or narrow customer bases. Formally, strategic planning models are most apt to be used by larger firms, and the models are adapted to the needs of the specific firms employing them.

The approaches' major strengths are that they let a firm analyze all SBUs and products, study the effects of various strategies, reveal the opportunities to pursue and the threats to avoid, compute marketing and other resource needs, focus on key differential advantages, compare performance with designated goals, and discover principles for improving. Competitors can also be studied.

The approaches' major weaknesses are that they may be hard to use (particularly by a small firm), may be too simplistic and omit key factors, are somewhat arbitrary in defining SBUs and evaluative criteria (such as relative market share), may not be applicable to all firms and situations (a dog SBU may be profitable and generate cash), do not adequately account for environmental conditions (such as the economy), may overvalue market share, and are often used by staff planners rather than line managers.

These techniques are only planning aids. They do not replace the need for managers to engage in hands-on decisions by studying each situation and basing marketing strategies on the unique aspects of their industry, firm, and SBUs.

IMPLEMENTING TACTICAL PLANS

A **tactical plan** specifies the short-run actions (tactics) that a firm undertakes in implementing a given marketing strategy. At this stage, a strategy is operationalized. A tactical plan has three basic elements: specific tasks, a time frame, and resource allocation.

The marketing mix (specific tasks) may range from a combination of high quality, high service, low distribution intensity, personal selling emphasis, and above-average prices to a combination of low quality, low service, high distribution intensity, advertising emphasis, and low prices. Each SBU should have a distinct marketing mix, based on its target market and strategic emphasis. The individual mix elements must be coordinated for each SBU, and conflicts among SBUs must be minimized.

Proper timing (time horizon) may mean being the first to introduce a product, bringing out a product when the market is most receptive, or quickly reacting to a competitor's strategy to catch it off guard. A firm must balance its desire to be an industry leader with clear-cut competitive advantages against its concern for the risk of being innovative. Marketing opportunities exist for limited times, and the firm needs to act accordingly.

Marketing investments (resources) may be order-processing or order-generating. Order-processing costs involve recording and handling orders, such as order entry, computer-data handling, and merchandise handling. The goal is to minimize those costs, subject to a given level of service. Order-generating costs, such as advertising and personal selling, produce revenues. Reducing them may be harmful to sales and profits. A firm should estimate sales at various levels of costs and for various combinations of marketing functions. Maximum profit rarely occurs at the lowest level of expenditure on order-generating costs.

Tactical decisions differ from strategic decisions in these ways. They:

- Are less complex and more structured.
- Have a much shorter time horizon.
- Require a considerably lower resource commitment.
- Are enacted and adjusted more often.

PepsiCo's Frito-Lay (**www.fritolay.com**) "is the undisputed chip champ of North America. The company makes some of the best-known and top-selling savory snacks around, including Cheetos, Doritos, Lay's, Ruffles, SunChips, and Tostitos. On the sweet side, Frito-Lay also makes Grandma's cookies, Funyuns onion-flavored rings, Cracker Jack candy-coated popcorn, and Smartfood popcorn. It also makes a line of chips made with the Light brand name."[21] At Frito-Lay, tactical planning means regularly introducing new versions of its products, informing delivery people and retailers about these products, aggressively promoting products, and maintaining profit margins—while not giving competitors a chance to win market share by maintaining lower prices, advertising heavily, and servicing retail accounts very well. On the other hand, small manufacturers may need outside food brokers to gain access to food retailers. Even then, they may have difficulty getting chains as customers.

MONITORING RESULTS

Monitoring results involves comparing the actual performance of a firm, business unit, or product against planned performance for a specified period. Actual performance data are then fed back into the strategic planning process. Budgets, timetables, sales and profit statistics, cost analyses, and image studies are just some measures that can be used to assess results.

When actual performance lags, corrective action is needed. For instance, "When it comes time to implement a strategy, many companies find themselves stymied at the point of execution. Having identified the opportunities within their reach, they watch as the results fall short of their aspirations. Too few companies recognize the reason. Mismatched capabilities, poor asset configurations, and inadequate execution can all play their part in undermining a company's strategic objectives."[22]

Some plans must be revised due to the impact of uncontrollable factors on sales and costs. For this reason, many farsighted firms develop contingency plans to outline their potential responses in advance, should unfavorable conditions arise.

These techniques are covered at the end of our book so that the fundamental elements of marketing are thoroughly explored first.

GLOBAL MARKETING IN PRACTICE

Companies, especially large ones, often enter foreign markets to ramp up their revenues and profits. Sometimes, they succeed and do so in a big way—as with General Motors in China. Other times, their marketing strategy just does not work well in a foreign market. This happened recently with giant British food retailer Tesco, which decided to exit the U.S. market after just a few years. Read "Britain's Tesco Exits the United States" (**http://wp.me/p1RDck-1Mr**) to see why.

DEVISING A STRATEGIC MARKETING PLAN

A firm can best create, implement, and monitor a strategic marketing plan when it has a written plan. This encourages executives to carefully think out and coordinate each step in the planning process, better pinpoint problem areas, be consistent, tie the plan to goals and resources, measure performance, and send a clear message to employees and others. It should not be too complicated to enact properly. See Figure 4.11. A sample outline for a written strategic plan and an application of strategic planning by a small firm are covered next.

"... And that, in a nutshell, is my marketing plan. Any questions?

Figure 4.11 Making a Marketing Strategy Too Complex
A good marketing plan can be easily understood and enacted, and is not overly confusing.
Source: Shutterstock. Reprinted by permission.

A SAMPLE OUTLINE FOR A WRITTEN STRATEGIC MARKETING PLAN

What are the ingredients of a good strategic marketing plan? It should:

- Be integrated into an organization's overall business plan.
- Affect the consideration of strategic choices.
- Express a long-range view.
- Make the resource allocation system visible.
- Provide methods to help strategic analysis and decision making.
- Be a basis for managing a firm or SBU strategically.
- Offer a communication and coordination system both horizontally (between SBUs and departments) and vertically (from senior executives to front-line employees).
- Help a firm and its SBUs cope with change.[23]

Table 4.2 presents a sample outline for a written strategic marketing plan. This outline may be used by firms of any size or type. (*Please note: There is a comprehensive strategic marketing plan template accompanying this book that is based on table 4.2. The template is described in the appendix at the end of chapter 4. At the beginning of each part of the text, the aspects of table 4.2 covered in that part are noted.*)

MOONSTRUCK CHOCOLATE COMPANY: A STRATEGIC MARKETING PLAN BY A SMALL SPECIALTY FIRM[24]

In 1993, Bill and Deb Simmons opened Moonstruck Chocolate Company (then known as Moonstruck Chocolatier) in Portland, Oregon. When it began, Moonstruck was exclusively a maker of truffles for the wholesale market. It sold to retailers such as Neiman Marcus, Marshall Field, and Starbucks. The firm introduced its first retail store in 1996, and sales rose rapidly. Today, Moonstruck is a successful firm that specializes in chocolate-based products, with annual sales of several million dollars and high-powered goals for the future. Why? The firm has created, implemented, and monitored a solid strategic marketing plan. Let's look at the highlights of Moonstruck's plan.

ORGANIZATIONAL MISSION

Moonstruck has a clear mission: To "handcraft superior chocolates—chocolates that would not only taste exquisite, but that would look exceptional, as well. The result would be a chocolate indulgence for all the senses." To do so, Moonstruck is "romancing" the cocoa bean and educating customers, as Starbucks did with coffee.

In 2001, Dave and Sally Bany acquired the firm. They were searching for a small business to take national: "One taste of Moonstruck's products and they were hooked. To make fitting use of a well-worn phrase, they liked it so much they bought the company." Since then the Banys have sought to grow the business. They are doing this now through its wholesale business (with products resold to retailers), direct sales (through 1-800-557-MOON), and sales from the Web site. They continue to have some company cafés.

ORGANIZATIONAL STRUCTURE

The Banys play a role in helping develop new products, planning marketing strategies, and ensuring overall quality. However, the firm is now headed by a professional staff that includes chief executive Dan Hossley, who has 30-plus years of retail experience, and "Master Chocolatier" Julian Rose, who also has 30-plus years of experience as a pastry chef and chocolatier. The firm's team of chocolatiers "quietly work away on a variety of confections, handcrafted, dipped, and decorated, ranging from toffee to truffles to chocolate bars."

MARKETING OBJECTIVES

After two decades, Moonstruck still has forward-looking goals. Sales have been increasing nicely due to the debut of various popular new chocolate lines, the expansion of the wholesale portion of its business, and the popularity of its Web site for sales. As Sally Bany says, "We want to be a national brand and we're well on our way to that as long as we keep making great products."

SITUATION ANALYSIS

Founders Bill and Deb Simmons formulated their strategic plan based on Starbucks. They did a comprehensive analysis of Starbucks' business model before opening Moonstruck, and were convinced that quality, carefully made chocolate could win a loyal following. Today, Moonstruck brings its distinctive design flourishes to the company Web site. It places far less emphasis on its own stores and much more on resellers.

DEVELOPING MARKETING STRATEGY

The two strategic planning approaches with the most relevance for Moonstruck are the product/market opportunity matrix and the Porter generic strategy model. The firm is engaged in both a product development strategy (producing distinctive new chocolate products for current chocolate customers) and a market development

TABLE 4.2 A SAMPLE OUTLINE FOR A WRITTEN STRATEGIC MARKETING PLAN

Using as much detail as possible, please address each of these points for your organization:

1. **Organizational Mission**

   a. In 50 words or less, describe the current mission of your organization.

   b. In 50 words or less, describe how you would like your organizational mission to evolve over the next 5 years. Over the next 10 years.

   c. How is the organizational mission communicated to employees?

2. **Organizational Structure**

   a. State and assess the current organizational structure of your organization.

   b. Does your organization have strategic business units? If yes, describe them. If no, why not?

   c. Does each major product or business unit in your organization have a marketing manager, proper resources, and clear competitors? Explain your answer.

3. **Marketing Objectives**

   a. Cite your organization's overall marketing goals for the next 1, 3, 5, and 10 years.

   b. Cite your organization's specific marketing goals by target market and product category for the next 1, 5, and 10 years in terms of sales, market share, profit, image, and customer loyalty.

   c. What criteria will be used to determine whether goals have been fully, partially, or unsatisfactorily reached?

4. **Situation Analysis**

   a. Describe the present overall strengths, weaknesses, opportunities, and threats (SWOT) facing your organization.

   b. For each of the key products or businesses of your organization, describe the present strengths, weaknesses, opportunities, and threats.

   c. How do you expect the factors noted in your answers to (a) and (b) to change over the next 5 to 10 years?

   d. How will your organization respond to the factors mentioned in the answer for (c)?

   e. Describe the methods your organization uses to acquire, distribute, and store the information necessary to make good marketing decisions.

5. **Developing Marketing Strategy**

   a. Compare your organization's overall strategy with those of leading competitors.

   b. Describe your organization's use of these strategic approaches: market penetration, market development, product development, and diversification.

   c. Categorize each of your organization's products or businesses as a star, cash cow, question mark, or dog. Explain your reasoning.

   d. For each product or business, which of these approaches is most appropriate: invest/grow, selectivity/earnings, or harvest/divest? Explain your reasoning.

   e. For each of your organization's products or businesses, which of these approaches is most appropriate: cost leadership, differentiation, cost focus, or differentiation focus? Explain your reasoning.

6. Societal, Ethical, and Consumer Issues

    a. What is your organization's view of its responsibilities regarding societal, ethical, and consumer issues?

    b. How are organizational policies developed with regard to societal, ethical, and consumer issues?

    c. Discuss your organization's social responsibility approach in terms of the general public, employees, channel members, stockholders, and competitors.

    d. State your organization's code of ethics and how acceptable ethical practices are communicated to employees.

    e. Describe your organization's strategy for dealing with consumers' basic rights (information and education, safety, choice, and to be heard).

7. Global Marketing

    a. What is the role of global marketing in your organization's overall strategy?

    b. Describe the cultural, economic, political and legal, and technological environment in each major and potential foreign market that your organization faces.

    c. Describe your organization's strategy in terms of which and how many foreign markets your organization should enter.

    d. Develop an appropriate organizational format for each current and potential foreign market.

    e. State the extent to which your organization utilizes a standardized, nonstandardized, or glocal (both global and local) marketing approach in its foreign markets.

    f. Explain how your organization's marketing mix varies by foreign market.

8. Marketing and the Internet

    a. Does your organization use the Internet (Web) in its marketing strategy? If no, why not?

    b. If your organization uses the Web, does it engage in E-marketing rather than just in E-commerce? If no, why not?

    c. If your organization uses the Web, what are the marketing-related goals?

    d. If your organization uses the Web, is a systematic Internet marketing strategy applied? If no, why not?

9. Consumer Analysis and Target Market Strategy

    a. What are the demographic characteristics of the target market segments served or potentially served by your organization?

    b. What are the lifestyle and decision-making characteristics of the target market segments served or potentially served by your organization?

    c. Do you market to final consumers, organizations, or both? How does this approach affect your overall marketing strategy?

    d. Describe the important consumer trends that could have a major effect on your organization.

    e. Explain the demand patterns that exist for your organization's products (homogeneous, clustered, or diffused).

(*continued*)

    f. Describe your organization's choice of target market strategy (undifferentiated, differentiated, or concentrated marketing) and target market(s).

    g. Does your organization understand and utilize such concepts as derived demand, the heavy-usage segment, and benefit segmentation? Why or why not?

    h. State how your marketing mix(es) is (are) appropriate for the target market(s) chosen.

    i. What sales forecasting procedures are used by your organization? How are they related to your target market strategy?

10. Product Planning

    a. Describe your organization's products from the perspective of tangible, augmented, and generic product concepts.

    b. Are your organization's products viewed as convenience, shopping, or specialty products by consumers? How does this placement affect the marketing strategy?

    c. Discuss the rationale behind the width, depth, and consistency of your organization's product mix.

    d. Describe your organization's product management organization.

    e. Discuss your organization's competitive and company product positioning for each product/brand.

    f. Describe your organization's use of corporate symbols and its branding strategy.

    g. Outline your organization's overall packaging strategy.

    h. What kinds of goods (durable and/or nondurable) and services (rented-goods, owned-goods, and/or nongoods) are sold by your organization? What are the ramifications of this for the marketing strategy?

    i. How are your organization's products positioned along the goods/service continuum? What are the ramifications of this for the marketing strategy?

    j. Describe your organization's new-product planning process.

    k. In what product life-cycle stage is each of your organization's major product groupings?

    l. How can your organization extend the life-cycle stage for those products now in the introduction, growth, and maturity life-cycle stages?

11. Distribution Planning

    a. How are channel functions allocated among distribution intermediaries and your organization?

    b. Explain how relationship marketing is used in your organization's channel of distribution.

    c. State your organization's distribution approach with regard to channel length (direct or indirect) and channel width (exclusive, selective, or intensive distribution), and whether a dual distribution strategy is appropriate.

    d. Present an approach for your organization's achieving and maintaining channel cooperation.

    e. Describe your organization's overall logistics strategy (including transportation modes, inventory management, and foreign distribution).

    f. Explain your organization's choice of wholesaler type and your choice of specific wholesalers.

    g. Explain your organization's choice of retailer type and your choice of specific retailers.

    h. How are wholesalers and retailers evaluated by your organization?

12. Promotion Planning

   a. State your organization's broad promotion goals and the importance of each one.

   b. Discuss your organization's overall promotion plan from the perspective of integrated marketing communications, and describe the roles of advertising, public relations, personal selling, and sales promotion at your organization.

   c. Describe how your organization determines its overall promotional budget.

   d. For each element of the promotional mix (advertising, public relations, personal selling, and sales promotion):

     • Set specific goals.

     • Assign responsibility.

     • Establish a budget.

     • Develop a strategy (such as themes/messages/selling techniques/promotions, media choice, timing, cooperative efforts).

     • Set criteria for assessing success or failure.

   e. Describe how your organization's promotion efforts vary by target market and product.

   f. At your organization, what is the role for new communications formats and technologies (such as the Web, electronic in-store point-of-purchase displays, and handheld computers for salespeople)?

13. Price Planning

   a. Explain your organization's overall pricing approach (price-based versus nonprice-based) and how you determine the "value" your organization provides to consumers.

   b. Categorize your organization's target market(s) in terms of price sensitivity, and state how this affects the pricing strategy.

   c. What is your organization's pricing philosophy for dealing with cost increases or decreases?

   d. What practices does your organization follow to ensure compliance with all government rules about pricing?

   e. Describe the role each channel member (including your organization) plays in setting prices.

   f. Explain the competitive pricing environment your organization faces.

   g. State your organization's specific pricing objectives.

   h. Describe your organization's price strategy with regard to its use of cost-based, demand-based, and/or competition-based pricing.

   i. When your organization implements a price strategy, which of these elements does it use: customary versus variable pricing, one-price versus flexible pricing, odd pricing, the price-quality association, leader pricing, multiple-unit pricing, price lining, price bundling, geographic pricing, purchase terms, and price adjustments?

(*continued*)

14. Integrating and Analyzing the Marketing Plan

a. Describe your organization's processes for integrating and analyzing its marketing plans.

b. Detail how the long-term, moderate-term, and short-term plans are compatible.

c. Explain how the elements of the marketing mix are coordinated.

d. Are ongoing marketing budgets sufficient? Does your organization differentiate between order-generating and order-processing costs? Explain your answers.

e. How do you expect competitors to react as you implement your organization's strategy?

f. Discuss how your organization utilizes benchmarking, customer satisfaction research, marketing cost analysis, sales analysis, and the marketing audit.

15. Revising the Marketing Plan

a. What contingency plans does your organization have in place for handling unexpected results?

b. Are marketing plans revised as conditions warrant? Explain your answer.

c. Is your organization reactive or proactive in its approach to revising marketing plans? Explain your answer.

Note: Points 1–5 relate to Part 1 in the text.

Points 6–8 relate to Part 2 in the text.

Point 9 relates to Part 3 in the text.

Point 10 relates to Part 4 in the text.

Point 11 relates to Part 5 in the text.

Point 12 relates to Part 6 in the text.

Point 13 relates to Part 7 in the text.

Points 14–15 relate to Part 8 in the text.

strategy (seeking out those who have not thought of chocolate beverages such as Mayan Hot Cocoa as "must have" drinks). It is a great believer in a differentiation strategy (superior products at a premium price).

SOCIETAL, ETHICAL, AND CONSUMER ISSUES

Moonstruck uses the highest-quality ingredients. It treats employees and customers courteously, honestly, and respectfully. The firm stands behind all of the products it makes and sells, and is socially responsible.

GLOBAL MARKETING

Moonstruck searches the globe for the best cocoa beans, consistent with its organizational mission: "Our chocolate products are made with only the finest, freshest ingredients. The company's chocolate originates from rare cocoa beans that are among the highest quality produced anywhere in the world. When properly fermented and roasted, the cocoa seeds achieve fine profiles of unique flavors with nuances of fresh flowers, ripe fruits, and rich woods."

MARKETING AND THE INTERNET

Moonstruck has a colorful, interactive, well-planned Web site (**www. moonstruckchocolate.com**) that describes the background of the company, customer service policies, and the products it makes. The site also lists the firm's retail locations and permits online ordering. There are even a couple of video clips. The company also uses Facebook (**www.facebook.com/moonstruckchocolate**) and Twitter (**www.twitter.com/MoonstruckChoc**).

CONSUMER ANALYSIS AND TARGET MARKET STRATEGY

Moonstruck appeals to customers who are interested in quality, uniqueness, assortment, and service—and are willing to pay for it. The firm has three market segments: Web and telephone shoppers (1-800-557-MOON) who buy directly from the firm, independent retailers (that typically buy through wholesalers) that sell Moonstruck products to their customers, and customers who buy at the firm's cafés.

PRODUCT PLANNING

Moonstruck has greatly expanded its product line since the early days, adding products that complement each other well. Today, the product line includes chocolate truffles, chocolate bars, chocolate pecan clusters, tangerine and blackberry truffles, tumbled chocolate, chocolate mints, toffee, hot cocoa mixes, chocolate and espresso drinks (at its cafés), and more.

DISTRIBUTION PLANNING

As already noted, Moonstruck offers products at many venues: retail stores, the Web, telemarketing, and its own cafés. Its five retail cafés now operate only in Oregon, as Moonstruck has closed its stores in other states to concentrate on sales through its Web site and through third-party retailers. The cafés feature the firm's moon logo, chocolate-colored swirls woven into the ceiling and carpeting, and seating for about 20 to 25 people. See figure 4.12. Whole Foods Market, Balducci's, and Amazon.com are among the retailers carrying Moonstruck products.

Figure 4.12 The Allure of Moonstruck Chocolate Cafés
Source: Reprinted by permission.

PROMOTION PLANNING

Moonstruck uses in-store tastings and demonstrations to draw customers into impulse purchases. It also does some print advertising and runs several seasonal events each year. But its biggest promotion effort revolves around the publicity it receives from newspaper, magazine, TV, and social media coverage. The *Ellen DeGeneres Show* has featured Moonstruck in the gift bags given to guest celebrities.

PRICE PLANNING

Moonstruck has above-average prices, reflective of the quality and status accorded its products. Most revenues are from high-margin chocolate truffles and drinks. For example, one 24-piece truffle collection in a special gift box retails for $50 and one 9-piece truffle collection in a standard box retails for $20.

INTEGRATING AND ANALYZING THE PLAN

The Banys and their management team constantly keep their eye on the ball. They recognize that every decision they make reflects on the image and performance of

Moonstruck Chocolate. They regularly monitor performance and look for ideas that fit within their overall vision for the firm.

REVISING THE MARKETING PLAN

Unlike Bill and Deb Simmons, the Banys are not big believers in franchising as a mechanism for future growth in Moonstruck Chocolate. As Dave Bany says, "I understand it's pretty difficult to control quality, and that makes me hesitant." Expansion will be mostly driven by the firm's Web site and third-party retailers.

CAREER TIPS

Strategic planning not only applies to organizations, it also applies to us in mapping out our career paths. What are our career goals? What are the career-related strengths, weaknesses, opportunities, and threats that we must recognize? What is our personal marketing mix? And so on.

WEB SITES YOU CAN USE

A variety of Web sites provide step-by-step advice on strategic planning, and many even have free, downloadable, easy-to-use templates. Here, we present a number of such sites, divided into two categories: strategic business plans and strategic marketing plans.

Strategic Business Plans

- BizMove.com: *Developing Your Own Business Plan* (**www.bizmove.com/starting/m1e1.htm**)
- Bplans.com—*How to Write a Business Plan* (**http://t.co/RSJjttHa5o**)
- Business Owner's Toolkit—*Writing Your Business Plan* (**http://t.co/7vceqTE8py**)
- Center for Business Planning—*Planning Guidelines* (**www.businessplans.org/guide.html**)
- Inc.—*Writing a Business Plan* (**www.inc.com/guides/write_biz_plan**)
- Edward Lowe Foundation—*How to Develop and Use a Business Plan* (**http://edwardlowe.org/erc/?ercID=7704**)
- PlanWare—*Writing a Business Plan* (**www.planware.org/bizplan.htm**)
- Tutor2You—*Strategy: What Is a Strategy?* (**http://t.co/QRTbQszNPP**)

Strategic Marketing Plans

- BizMove.com—*Small Business Marketing* (**http://t.co/wINjQ2ptdB**)
- Bplans.com—*Sample Marketing Plans* (**http://t.co/tP1KUn2nQN**)
- Business Resource Software—*Marketing Plan* (**www.businessplans.org/Market.html**)
- Inc.—*Marketing Guides* (**www.inc.com/guides/marketing**)
- Edward Lowe Foundation—*How to Gain a Competitive Edge* (**http://edwardlowe.org/erc/?ercID=8869**)
- Morebusiness.com—*Marketing* (**www.morebusiness.com/marketing**)
- Morebusiness.com—*Sample Marketing Plan* (**http://t.co/pe7rjwaYqP**)
- U.S. Chamber of Commerce—*Building a Successful Marketing Plan* (**http://uschambersmallbusinessnation.com/start/**)

SUMMARY

1. *To define strategic planning and consider its importance for marketing* Strategic planning encompasses both strategic business plans and strategic marketing plans. Strategic business plans describe the overall direction firms will pursue within their chosen environment and guide the allocation of resources and effort. Strategic marketing plans outline what marketing actions to undertake, why those actions are needed, who is responsible for carrying them out, when and where they will be completed, and how they will be coordinated.

   Strategic planning provides guidance via a hierarchical process, clarifies goals, encourages departmental cooperation, focuses on strengths and weaknesses (as well as opportunities and threats), examines alternatives, helps allocate resources, and points out the value of monitoring results.

2. *To describe the total quality approach to strategic planning and show its relevance to marketing* A total quality approach should be used in devising and enacting business and marketing plans. In that way, a firm adopts a process- and output-related philosophy, by which it strives to fully satisfy consumers in an effective and efficient manner. Customer focus; top management commitment; emphasis on continuous improvement; and support and involvement from employees, suppliers, and channel members are all involved.

3. *To look at the different kinds of strategic plans and the relationships between marketing and the other functional areas in an organization* A firm's strategic plans may be short-run, moderate in length, or long-run. Strategic marketing plans may be for each major product, presented as one company-wide marketing plan, or considered part of an overall business plan. A bottom-up, top-down, or combined management approach may be used.

The interests of marketing and the other functional areas in a firm need to be accommodated in a strategic plan. Departmental conflict can be reduced by improving communications, employing personnel with broad backgrounds, establishing interdepartmental programs, and blending departmental goals.

4. *To describe thoroughly each of the steps in the strategic planning process* First, a firm defines its organizational mission—the long-term commitment to a type of business and a place in the market. Second, it establishes strategic business units (SBUs), the self-contained divisions, product lines, or product departments with specific market focuses and separate managers. Third, quantitative and qualitative marketing objectives are set. Fourth, through situation analysis, a firm identifies its internal strengths and weaknesses, as well as external opportunities and threats.

Fifth, a firm develops a marketing strategy—to outline the way in which the marketing mix is used to attract and satisfy the target market(s) and accomplish organizational goals. Every SBU has its own marketing mix. The approaches to strategy planning include the product/market opportunity matrix, the Boston Consulting Group matrix, the General Electric business screen, and the Porter generic strategy model. They should be viewed as planning tools that aid decision making; they do not replace the need for executives to engage in hands-on planning for each situation.

Sixth, a firm uses tactical plans to specify the short-run actions necessary to implement a given marketing strategy. At this stage, specific tasks, a time horizon, and resource allocation are made operational. Seventh, a firm monitors results by comparing actual performance against planned performance, and this information is fed back into the strategic planning process. Adjustments in strategy are made as needed.

5. *To show how a strategic marketing plan may be devised and applied* Strategic marketing plans work best when they are integrated within the overall strategic business plan and prepared systematically and comprehensively—as illustrated in table 4.2. This is exemplified by Moonstruck Chocolate, a small confectionary firm.

KEY TERMS

strategic business plan (p. 92)

strategic marketing plan (p. 92)

total quality (p. 95)

strategic planning process (p. 100)

organizational mission (p. 101)

strategic business unit (SBU) (p. 103)

situation analysis (p. 105)

marketing strategy (p. 107)

product/market opportunity matrix (p. 108)

Boston Consulting Group matrix (p. 110)

General Electric business screen (p. 112)

Porter generic strategy model (p. 114)

tactical plan (p. 117)

monitoring results (p. 118)

1. Distinguish between the terms "strategic business plan" and "strategic marketing plan."

2. Explain figure 4.4, which deals with the total quality approach.

3. Why are conflicts between marketing and other functional areas inevitable? How can these conflicts be reduced or avoided?

4. Under what circumstances should a company consider reappraising its organizational mission?

5. In situation analysis, what is the distinction between strengths and opportunities and between weaknesses and threats? How should a firm react to each of these factors?

6. Distinguish between the Boston Consulting Group matrix and the Porter generic strategy model.

7. Explain how tactical decisions differ from strategic decisions.

8. Why is it important to monitor the results of a marketing plan?

DISCUSSION QUESTIONS

1. Do you think your college bookstore is following a total quality approach? Why or why not? What total quality recommendations would you make for the bookstore?

2. What issues should a movie studio study during situation analysis? How could it react to those issues?

3. Give a current example of each of these strategic approaches: market development, product development, market penetration, and diversification. Evaluate the strategies.

4. Develop a rating scale to use in analyzing the industry attractiveness and company business strengths of a leading DVD manufacturer or a medium-sized toy manufacturer.

Bplans.com (**http://t.co/tP1KUn2nQN**) offers several free sample marketing plans at its Web site. Take a look at the sample marketing plan for The Tooth Fairy (**http://t.co/OdBlzKqz6T**), a dental practice. What could a prospective competitor learn from studying this plan?

PRACTICE QUIZ

1. An organization's direction within its chosen environment and its allocation of resources is usually determined by:

    a. strategic planning.

    b. strategic business units.

    c. marketing tactics.

    d. marketing myopia.

2. Separate marketing plans for each product line are most often used by:

    a. local governments.

    b. consumer-goods manufacturers.

    c. service firms.

    d. industrial-goods manufacturers.

3. Which of these is a way to reduce tension among functional departments?

    a. Minimizing interfunctional contact

    b. Seeking employees who do not blend technical and marketing expertise

    c. Establishing independent task forces and committees

    d. Setting objectives for each department interdependent with other departments' goals

4. Organizational mission refers to:

   a. a philosophy by which an organization individually assesses and positions every SBU.

   b. a long-term commitment to a type of business and a place in the market.

   c. specific actions undertaken to implement a given marketing strategy.

   d. an approach in which a firm seeks greater sales of present products or new product uses.

5. In the strategic planning process, the next step after a firm defines its organizational mission is to:

   a. outline a budget.

   b. establish strategic business units.

   c. set marketing objectives.

   d. perform situation analysis.

6. An example of a qualitative term that can be used to describe objectives is:

   a. market share in the industry.

   b. profit as a percentage of sales.

   c. sales growth.

   d. level of innovativeness.

7. Which of the following questions does situation analysis seek to answer?

    a. In what direction is a firm headed?

    b. How will resources be allocated?

    c. Who is responsible for carrying out marketing actions?

    d. What sales personnel should be hired?

8. As part of a market development strategy, a firm could:

    a. develop new models of existing products to appeal to present markets.

    b. reposition existing products.

    c. become involved with new products aimed at new markets.

    d. seek to attract nonusers of its existing products.

9. A strategic business unit with a high market share in a mature industry is a:

    a. question mark.

    b. cash cow.

    c. star.

    d. dog.

10. The General Electric business screen looks at two major dimensions: company business strengths and:

    a. market share.

    b. profitability.

c. industry attractiveness.

d. target market features.

11. Strategic business units shown in the selectivity/earnings areas of the General Electric business screen are:

a. performing poorly in unattractive industries.

b. performing poorly in highly competitive industries.

c. performing well in unattractive industries.

d. performing well in strong industries.

12. According to the Porter generic strategy model, with a differentiation focus strategy, a strategic business unit:

a. aims at a narrow target segment through low prices or a unique offering.

b. aims at a broad market and offers products at low prices and in large quantities.

c. aims at a narrow market by offering goods or services viewed as distinctive.

d. aims a new product at a new market

13. A major weakness of the strategic planning approaches discussed in this chapter is that they:

a. are sometimes difficult to implement.

b. do not allow a firm to follow competitors' actions.

c. prevent a firm from analyzing all its business units and products.

d. do not focus on creating and keeping key differential advantages.

14. The level of investment in specific marketing activities and the timing of marketing actions are decisions relating to:

    a. implementing tactics.

    b. establishing SBUs.

    c. developing marketing strategy.

    d. monitoring results.

15. Monitoring results involves:

    a. setting corporate and marketing objectives.

    b. creating new strategic business units.

    c. comparing actual performance to planned performance for a specified time period.

    d. identifying internal strengths and weaknesses, as well as external opportunities and threats.

For the answers to these questions, please visit the online site for this book at **http://www.textbookmedia.com/textbook/LearnMores/EvansBermanAnswersAndExercises.pdf**.

NOTES

1. "Dictionary," **http://www.marketingpower.com/_layouts/Dictionary.aspx?dLetter=S** (March 2, 2014). For background information on strategic planning, see "Strategic Planning," **www.bain.com/publications/articles/management-tools- strategic-planning.aspx** (March 8, 2013).

2. "Aspects of Strategic Marketing," **www.zabanga.info/marketing-planning/aspects-of-strategic-marketing.html** (July 1, 2013).

3. "Ritz-Carlton: Gold Standards," **http://corporate.ritzcarlton.com/en/About/GoldStandards.htm** (February 8, 2014).

4. "Excellent Global Corporation Plan Phase IV," **www.canon.com/about/strategies** (November 9, 2013).

5. "Dictionary," **www.marketingpower.com/_layouts/Dictionary.aspx?dLetter=C** (March 2, 2014).

6. "Strategizing for 2013—Mission Statements," **http://rppc.net/strategizing-for-2013-mission-statements** (September 14, 2013).

7. "Southwest Airlines: Customer Service Commitment," **www.southwest.com/assets/pdfs/corporate-commitments/customer-service-commitment.pdf** (May 10, 2013).

8. "Our Company," **www.jnj.com/about-jnj** (April 3, 2014).

9. "About HP," **http://www8.hp.com/us/en/hp-information/index.html** (August 5, 2013).

10. "HP: Our Corporate Objectives," **http://www8.hp.com/us/en/hp-information/about-hp/corporate-objectives.html** (August 5, 2013).

11. "Company Profile: The Procter & Gamble Company," *MarketLine* (July 2, 2013), pp. 4–5.

12. Adapted by the authors from Advanced Integrated Technologies, "SWOT Analysis," **www.scribd.com/doc/2673524/SWOT-Analysis** (2006).

13. "General Mills, Inc. Company Information," **http://t.co/OhILRJZTEm** (February 2, 2014).

14. H. Igor Ansoff, "Strategies for Diversification," *Harvard Business Review*, Vol. 35 (September–October 1957), pp. 113–124. See also "The Ansoff Matrix—Problem-Solving Training from MindTools.com," **http://shar.es/ytsL0** (October 9, 2013).

15. Various sections, **www.ups.com** (March 3, 2014).

16. For more information, see Ovidijus Jurevicius, "BCG Growth-Share Matrix," **http://t.co/3PXUyg21j3** (May 1, 2013); and "The Boston Matrix—Strategy Tools From Mind-Tools.com," **http://shar.es/yvY7T** (March 2, 2014).

17. Authors' analysis based on various reports.

18. "Marketing Strategy Matrix," **http://www.brs-inc.com/models/model17.asp** (August 9, 2013); and David A. Aaker, *Strategic Marketing Management*, Tenth Edition (New York: Wiley, 2013).

19. "About Bausch & Lomb," **www.bausch.com/en/Our-Company/About-Bausch-And-Lomb** (October 3, 2013).

20. Michael E. Porter, *Competitive Advantage: Creating and Sustaining Superior Performance* (New York: Free Press, 1985), pp. 11–26; Michael E. Porter, *Competitive Strategy: Techniques for Analyzing Industries and Competitors* (New York: Free Press, 1980), pp. 34–46; and "Porter's Generic Strategies—Strategy Skills Training from MindTools.com," **http://shar.es/y5IJ6** (March 2, 2014).

21. "Frito-Lay, Inc.," **http://t.co/yqimYsintV** (March 9, 2014).

22. Tsun-yan Hsieh and Sara Yik, "Leadership as the Starting Point of Strategy," *McKinsey Quarterly*, **http://shar.es/y5T2E** (November 1, 2005).

23. Adapted by the authors from Aaker, *Strategic Marketing Management*.

24. The material in this section is based on **www.moonstruck-chocolate.com** (March 7, 2014); Elizabeth Fuhrman, "A New Moon," *Candy Industry* (June 2004), pp. 28–33; Edward O. Welles, "The Next Starbucks," *Inc.* (January 2001), pp. 48–53; "Moonstruck Chocolate Co. Selects New CEO," *Portland Business Journal*, **http://t.co/bcqp0Za8Dh** (March 25, 2008); "Moonstruck Chocolate Co. Commemorates 20th Anniversary," **http://bit.ly/Y4R1hl** (March 25, 2013); InsideView: Moonstruck Chocolate Co.," **www.insideview.com/directory/moonstruck-chocolate-co** (July 20, 2013); and "Moonstruck Chocolate," **http://topics.oregonlive.com/tag/Moonstruck Chocolate/index.html** (ongoing).

CHAPTER 4 APPENDIX: STRATEGIC MARKETING PLAN TEMPLATE

In chapter 4, we presented a detailed sample outline for preparing a written strategic marketing plan (table 4.3). Throughout *Marketing*, the part-opening pages refer to the specific sections of the sample plan that apply to each of the eight parts in the book.

To provide you with more insight into strategic marketing plans, we have prepared the special PDF-based template that is described in this appendix. It is called *Strategic Marketing Plan Template*. You may access the template at the book Web site.

Strategic Marketing Plan Template is based on the sample outline in chapter 4. From that outline, we have selected a cross section of questions for you to address. You will be assigned to a specific firm and gear your answers toward it. Answers are typed directly into easy-to-use drop-down windows. The exercise outline is shown in table 4.3.

By answering all *Strategic Marketing Plan Template* questions, you are preparing a comprehensive strategic marketing plan. Depending on your professor's goals, different students or student teams can be assigned to competing companies in the same industry—or assigned to companies with totally different strategies and resources. One student or team can be assigned to a national firm selling mass-appeal products, while another group is assigned to a local firm selling a product for a niche market.

You are encouraged to use secondary sources (including the Web) to devise a marketing plan when working on the *Strategic Marketing Plan Template* exercise. SWOT analysis (strengths, weaknesses, opportunities, and threats) should include data derived from secondary sources.

There are two ways in which your professor can assign the *Strategic Marketing Plan Template*: (1) You or a team of students can be requested to hand in *Strategic Marketing Plan Template* assignments one part at a time, with submissions spaced out over the term. (2) You or a team of students can be requested to work on *Strategic Marketing Plan Template* as a comprehensive course assignment, with one overall submission at the end of the semester.

TABLE 4.3 *STRATEGIC MARKETING PLAN TEMPLATE* OUTLINE

Develop an integrated strategic marketing plan for the assigned company by addressing each of the questions below.

Organizational Mission

- In 50 words or less, describe the current mission of your organization.

Marketing Goals

- Cite your organization's overall marketing goals for the next 1, 3, 5, and 10 years.

Situation Analysis

- Describe the present overall strengths, weaknesses, opportunities, and threats (SWOT) facing your organization.

Developing Marketing Strategy

- Compare your organization's overall strategy with those of leading competitors.

Societal, Ethical, and Consumer Issues

- What is your organization's view of its responsibilities regarding societal, ethical, and consumer issues?

Global Marketing

- What is the role of global marketing in your organization's overall strategy?

Marketing and the Internet

- Does your organization use the Internet (Web) in its marketing strategy? If so, how? If no, why not?

Consumer Analysis and Target Market Strategy

- What are the demographic characteristics of the target market segments served or potentially served by your organization?
- Do you market to final consumers, organizations, or both? How does this approach affect your overall marketing strategy?
- Describe your organization's choice of target market strategy (undifferentiated, differentiated, or concentrated marketing) and target market(s).

Product Planning

- Describe your organization's products from the perspective of tangible, augmented, and generic product concepts.
- Discuss the rationale behind the width, depth, and consistency of your organization's product mix.

Distribution Planning

- Explain how relationship marketing is used in your organization's channel of distribution.
- State your organization's distribution approach with regard to channel length (direct or indirect) and channel width (exclusive, selective, or intensive distribution), and whether a dual distribution strategy is appropriate.

Promotion Planning

- State your organization's broad promotion goals and the importance of each one.
- Discuss your organization's overall promotional plan from the perspective of integrated marketing communications, and describe the roles of advertising, public relations, personal selling, and sales promotion at your organization.

TABLE 4.3 *STRATEGIC MARKETING PLAN TEMPLATE* OUTLINE (*Continued*)

Price Planning

- Explain your organization's overall pricing approach (price-based versus nonprice-based) and how you determine the "value" your organization provides to consumers.
- Categorize your organization's target market(s) in terms of price sensitivity, and state how this affects the pricing strategy.

Integrating and Organizing the Marketing Plan

- How do you expect competitors to react as you implement your organization's strategy?

Revising the Marketing Plan

- What contingency plans does your organization have in place for handling unexpected results?

NOTE

We have included in the *Strategic Marketing Plan Template* an illustration of a strategic marketing plan for Sporting Goods and More, based on the Table 4.3 questions in this appendix. Assume that Sporting Goods and More is a large (40,000 square feet), privately owned, for-profit store located near a major shopping mall that is 5 to 10 miles from your campus. This retailer competes with all nearby firms that carry sporting goods, sports apparel, sports-related consumer electronics, sports-related publications, sports drinks and snacks, and similar merchandise. Although the specific answers in this illustration may not be directly applicable to another company, the example should stimulate your thinking and give you a better idea of how to handle the questions.

REFLECTIONS ON THE READING SELECTION

We offer the following editorial commentary on the reading selection.

1. Before the strategic planning process can begin, organizations need to evaluate their existing mission statement to make sure it accurately represents the mission of the organization. The website https://www.missionstatements.com/hospital_mission_statements.html offers many examples of good mission statements, but we believe the example below represents a patient-focused mission statement.

2. On the Practice Quiz on p. 134-138, the link on p. 138 is no longer active. Here are the answers to the Practice Quiz: 1. a, 2. b, 3. d, 4. b, 5. b, 6. d, 7. a, 8. d, 9. b, 10. c, 11. b and c, 12. c, 13. a, 14. a, 15. c.

Beth Israel Deaconess Medical Center http://www.bidmc.org/About-BIDMC/ Mission-and-Leadership.aspx

Mission and Leadership

Our mission at Beth Israel Deaconess Medical Center is to provide extraordinary care, where the patient comes first, supported by world-class education and research.

Our Mission

To provide extraordinary care, where the patient comes first, supported by world-class education and research.

The mission of Beth Israel Deaconess Medical Center is to serve our patients compassionately and effectively and to create a healthy future for them and their families. Our mission is supported by our commitment to provide personalized excellent care for our patients and a workforce committed to individual accountability, mutual respect, and collaboration.

We recognize that the diversity, talent, innovation, and commitment of all of our employees contribute to our strength and are a major component of our success. We greatly value the leadership and participation of our trustees, overseers, and donors who make an invaluable contribution to our ability to carry out our mission to serve patients, students, science, and our community.

3. On p. 105 of the reading, a SWOT analysis is discussed. Here is an example of a SWOT for a healthcare organization:

Strengths—Internal	Weaknesses—Internal
Recognized expertise	Difficulty retaining and attracting qualified personnel and staff
Quality of healthcare personnel/staff	
Strong administration	Poor communication
Member of an established healthcare system	Weak infrastructure (technical, facilities, etc.)
Strong, positive organizational culture	
Healthcare system brand recognition	

Opportunities—External	Threats—External
Aging population	Healthcare reform
Specializations	Governmental regulations
Develop strong brand name	Increased competition
	Power of insurance companies in negotiating fee schedules

APPLICATION AND SYNTHESIS

"Set your sights on the next decade, not the next day. Don't get bogged down in every single crisis—you need to not only focus on the incoming, but moving ahead."
—Cecil Richards, president of Planned Parenthood Federation of America & Planned Parenthood Action Fund in New York (Beckers Hospital Review, 2015)

QUESTIONS FOR DISCUSSION

1. What is your organization's mission statement? Does it accurately reflect the mission of your organization?

2. What are the most important aspects of your organization's total quality program?

3. Setting marketing objectives for healthcare organizations can be a sensitive topic when the focus is on providing quality healthcare. Is it appropriate for a healthcare organization to focus on marketing objectives?

4. What product/market opportunities exist for your organization? Using the product/market matrix, which strategy is most appropriate?

5. How could the Boston Consulting Group matrix be used in a healthcare organization?

6. How does the Boston Consulting Group matrix differ from the General Electric Business Screen and the Porter Generic Strategy Model?

SUMMARY OF MAIN POINTS

After reading this chapter, you should be able to:

√ Discuss how organizations use strategic planning (p. 95-99)
√ Identify the steps in the strategic planning process (p. 100)
√ Apply the Boston Consulting Group matrix to a healthcare organization (p. 110)

COMPREHENSION ASSESSMENT

1. What is the difference between a business plan and a marketing plan?

2. Explain the total quality approach to strategic planning.

3. What are the characteristics of a strategic business unit (SBU)?

4. Create a SWOT analysis for a healthcare organization.

5. What are the four marketing strategies in the product/market opportunity matrix?

6. How does an organization use the Boston Consulting Group (BCG) matrix?

7. What is the difference between the BCG matrix and the General Electric business screen?

8. How does the Porter Generic Strategy Model use competitive scope and competitive advantage?

CONCLUSION

In this chapter, we discussed the strategic planning process and the process involved with developing a marketing plan. These topics should be the foundational principles on which to base all marketing decisions within an organization. It is important to develop a marketing plan that will guide all of the marketing decisions that will help the organization achieve its strategic goals and objectives.

The next chapter will focus on creating value by listening. With the increasing emphasis on patient-centered healthcare, it is critical to understand how to improve the overall patient satisfaction with the healthcare experience by actively and compassionately listening to the patient and their family members.

REFERENCES

Beckers Hospital Review (2015). Retrieved from http://www.beckershospitalreview.com/hospital-management-administration/on-the-record-50-best-healthcare-quotes-of-2015.html.

KEY TERMS

Strategic planning includes both a **strategic business plan** and a **strategic marketing plan**.

Marketing should have a key role in strategic planning.

All firms should adopt a **total quality** approach, thereby becoming more process- and output-related in satisfying consumers.

For a total quality program to work, every party in the process must participate.

Short-run plans are precise; long-run plans outline needs.

Consumer-products firms often have plans for each line.

Bottom-up plans foster employee input; top-down plans are set by top management.

The perspectives of marketing and other functional areas need to be reconciled.

The **strategic planning process** includes steps from defining a mission to monitoring results.

A firm sets its direction in an **organizational mission**.

Strategic business units (SBUs) are separate operating units in an organization.

Marketing objectives may include quantitative and qualitative measures.

Situation analysis investigates a firm's strengths, weaknesses, opportunities, and threats.

A good **marketing strategy** provides a framework for marketing activities.

The **product/market opportunity matrix** involves market penetration, market development, product development, and diversification options.

The **Boston Consulting Group matrix** uses market share and industry growth to describe stars, cash cows, question marks, and dogs.

The **General Electric business screen** measures industry attractiveness and company business strengths.

The **Porter generic strategy model** distinguishes among cost leadership, differentiation, and focus strategies.

Strategic models have pros and cons, and should be only part of planning.

A marketing strategy is enacted via **tactical plans**.

Performance is evaluated by **monitoring results**.

Written documents aid strategic marketing planning and are useful for all sorts of firms.

Although a small company, Moonstruck Chocolate has a detailed strategic marketing plan.

IMAGE CREDITS

5 CHAPTER

CREATING VALUE BY LISTENING

LEARNING OBJECTIVES

In this chapter, you will learn about the following:

- The service encounter as the moment of truth
- The importance of listening
- The value of word of mouth (WOM)

INTRODUCTION

Henkel and Maryland (2015) discussed the paradigm shift in healthcare from volume-based to value-based medical care when they stated, "Not only must they reimagine how they identify, engage, and manage the care of patients, they also need to determine new ways of engaging and aligning physicians and other caregivers in creating better-coordinated care across the continuum." (p. 3).

The first step in creating value in the patient experience is to listen. This requires a shift in paradigm from volume-based to value-based medical care. Too often, medical providers focus solely on providing quality care in the most efficient manner, resulting in insufficient time being devoted to actually listening to the patient and their support system. For a patient to feel valued, they must believe that their healthcare provider is not only compassionate and empathetic, but also that they are focused on the patient as a person, not just resolving the immediate medical problem at hand.

NOTES FROM PRACTICE

Figure 5.1 John Frank Harper

As a young man, I observed people around me and read books to try to decide what profession I would follow.

While living in Pecos, a small West Texas town, I had a life-changing experience. My father, who had always been my hero, was a very tall, athletic man who seemed to be invulnerable to illness. While in Pecos, however, he developed illnesses that caused him to have frequent bouts of severe pain. These frightened me tremendously. I vividly remember hearing my father cry out in agony in the late hours of the night and watching my mother call the local primary care doctor, asking him to come to the house. She would say, "Bruce, Frank is in terrible pain. Could you send him something out to relieve his pain?" Rather than sending something out, he would arrive a few minutes later dressed in a three-piece suit with a neatly knotted tie and carrying a black bag full of medical equipment and medicines. He would then quietly greet my mother and me, go to the bedside of my father, put his hand softly on his shoulder, and say, "Frank, it's okay—I'm here now, and I'll stay until you're better." He then would stay and minister to my father until he was relieved of pain. He ministered not only to my father, but to my mother and to me! As I observed this scene, I saw an exquisite blend of a bright medical mind with sincere compassion. I remember saying to myself, "This is what I would like to do with my life."

Medicine is practiced best when it is evidence-based—that is where our actions are guided by evidence, which comes from good scientific studies. Such practice is necessary for good medicine, but not sufficient. Compassion is also a necessary, but not sufficient component. Medicine is practiced best when science and compassion intersect at the bedside of a patient.

I have found literature about medicine to be very helpful in trying to understand this dialectic. I found that reading about patients, reading about doctors, reading about the history of medicine, and reading about being a patient or a caregiver expanded my ability to combine these elements. Medicine is, after all, largely about listening, interpreting, and communicating with patients and families. Good literature enhances our ability to do all three. Literature about medicine can be written by physicians, nurses, patients, family members, or any keen observer of the medical situation. It is my belief that the reading of literature may make us "better people," and "better people" make "better doctors."

I am often asked, "What is the value of literature about medicine? Why is reading important to being a doctor?"

Responses include:

Reading:

- Is safe. I have never had to see a patient in an emergency room with a reading injury.
- Is relatively inexpensive.
- Is repeatable. I have read some books countless times and discover new ideas and nuances each time. I have read *Good-bye Mr. Chips*[1] by James Hilton many times. I weep each time as I read the last pages, which movingly describe the essence of Mr. Chips' life as a teacher of boys.
- Entertains and diverts us from the harsh realities of the life we live.
- Provokes and challenges us to think of our lives and goals differently. It expands our minds. The reading of Tracy Kidder's *Mountains Beyond Mountains* has catalyzed change in the life-view of countless medical residents, causing them to reevaluate their motives, actions, and goals for their future medical lives.
- Takes us geographically to places we can't physically visit. We can be anywhere in the world, in any circumstance, at any time in history without leaving our chair.
- Promotes self-expression and visualization.
- Helps us understand other ethnic, religious, and political groups. We better understand their needs, their expectations, and their family relationships.
- Helps us learn from mistakes of others so that we don't have to repeat them ourselves.
- Helps us deal with our own mistakes that may lead to shame.
- Teaches us ways to apologize as we read about others dealing with their mistakes and slights.

- Refreshes our reading and listening skills. A doctor must listen to the story a patient is telling because a patient desires that it be heard. Listening to the read word reinvigorates our listening skills—less often practiced than in times past.
- Challenges us to write and create literature ourselves.
- Ties us to our medical heritage and to the history of medicine. It allows us to "sit at the feet of giants," those who have preceded us in medicine, and reminds that there is really "nothing new under the sun."
- Frees us from the constant necessity to subject all information to a statistical analysis to authenticate validity. We are free to imagine and create our own view of the world. No Chi-square test or P-value is required.

Well-crafted essays and poems often synthesize difficult and complex problems and responses. As readers, we can utilize these synthetic concepts to more effectively communicate with our patients. Not long ago, I had a patient hospitalized for 12 weeks with a severe, life-threatening illness that required our medical team's highest level of attention and expertise to ensure his survival. At the first follow-up visit, the concerned wife thanked us for helping her husband survive but questioned why I had "been so serious" when I talked with them in the hospital. She was aware that in other circumstances, I was friendly and outgoing. I knew that I could describe in detail the intricacies of care, the sepsis, the powerful medicines utilized, the coma scales that predicted a poor prognosis, and the extensive antibiotic regimen we used to reflect the severity of his illness. This would have been an incomprehensible, prolonged explanation. It dawned on me that a quote from a poem by Antonio Machado that I found in the introduction to an essay by Dr. Lawrence Hergott would synthesize all these issues into a clear reason for my seriousness during the patient's illness. I quietly quoted, "The sound of a coffin hitting the earth is a sound utterly serious." She paused, looked pale, and uttered "Oh." The synthetic power of this single sentence said far more than I could have said in 20 minutes describing the clinical crises her husband had faced. It expressed the seriousness of our profession.

As I expressed these concepts to medical residents at my weekly conference, "Coffee with Cardiology," many were challenged and voiced a desire for further exploration of the topic. In addition, I found that many attending physicians were "kindred spirits" who found this concept interesting. These common interests led to a Literature and Medicine course for our residents and a yearly Literature and Medicine conference, "Intersections—Science and Compassion Intersecting at the Bedside—the Role of Literature." At our yearly meeting, we engage a distinguished guest speaker. We have had Pulitzer Prize-winning authors, Hippocrates Award-winning poets, and notable physician authors speak. The meeting has proven to be highly successful.

Figure 5.2 The Art is Hearing the Story

An outgrowth of the meeting has been the initiation of a writing contest. Each year, we have a juried award for the best original essay, short story, and poem. There is also a grand prize winner. Cash prizes are awarded. We have had entries from many countries around the world and all over the United States. The writings have been exceptional, with many examples of fine prose and poetry being submitted. This has been an exciting opportunity for the writers, but it also has been a great pleasure for the judges and readers of these pieces.

Literature helps us in a difficult world of being a physician to strive to bring science and compassion together at the bedside of our patients. When this is done well, medicine remains, as it should be, a noble profession.

REFERENCES

Hilton, James (1934). *Goodbye Mr. Chips*. New York: Little, Brown.

Hergott, Lawrence (2002). Playing the Moonlight Sonata from memory. *Journal of the American Medical Association, 28*(20), p. 2516.

Machado, Antonio (2004). The burial of a friend. In *Border of a Dream*, p. 13.

Kidder, Tracy (2004). *Mountains beyond mountains*. New York: Random House Trade Paperbacks.

SERVICE ENCOUNTERS AS A MOMENT OF TRUTH

A moment of truth is any time the patient interacts with the healthcare provider, giving the patient the chance to form an impression. Each time the patient or family member interacts with any employee within the healthcare organization, it is a moment of truth. This makes the complexity of the hospital service encounter even more difficult due to the number of different "touch points" a patient receives throughout their hospital stay.

Figure 5.3 The Power of a Story

These interactions can create moments of magic or moments of misery. A moment of magic is when the expectations of the patient are exceeded, while a moment of misery is created when the patient or family has a perception that their expectations are not being met. An *expectation* is what the patient or family member expects to happen based on their previous experiences, information, or personal beliefs. All of these small moments of truth lead to an overall impression of the patient experience.

LISTENING

Most of us probably believe we are good listeners; however, the listening process is actually much more involved. Listening encompasses words and sounds, but more importantly, it includes the meaning that we attach to those words. There are four stages of listening: attending, interpreting, responding, and remembering (Study.com). In the *attending* stage, we are merely collecting the sentences we hear for further analysis. Providers use the history and physical portion of their examination to gather information about the patient's medical problem and previous medical history. The *interpreting* stage is when we apply our own meaning to what we have heard. Our prior knowledge and experiences impact the meaning we assign to what we hear. Medical providers are usually quite proficient, interpreting what they hear to form an appropriate diagnosis. The third stage, *responding*, is how we react to what we have heard through both verbal and nonverbal responses. This is the stage where most healthcare providers fall short because they may not realize the effect of their communications with the patient and their family members. For example, abrupt responses regarding their medical assessment and the potential complications of a diagnosis may be stated without emotion or concern for how patients may receive this information. The final stage, *remembering*, is where we save the information we have gathered for future use.

It is important to acknowledge the goals of listening: appreciation, comprehension, empathy, and evaluation. Listening is a skill similar to reading, writing, and speaking, but although it is the most used, it is typically the one least taught. However, it is encouraging that one can become an effective listener with practice. Some tips to improve listening skills include being attentive as an active listener, having an open mind, staying present in the conversation, and not plotting what you will say next while the person is speaking.

If you are interested in evaluating your listening skills, we suggest you take the quick test "How Good Are Your Listening Skills": https://www.mindtools.com/pages/article/listening-quiz.htm.

WORD OF MOUTH (WOM)

In marketing, word of mouth (WOM) is often the most overlooked tool in the marketer's toolbox. Word of mouth in healthcare occurs when a satisfied or dissatisfied patient or family member tells others (family, friends, etc.) about their experience. With the prevalence of social media usage, WOM has even more serious implications for impression management. Previously, WOM was typically shared person-to-person, whereas with social media, the number of people that are connected either directly or indirectly to each other has increased significantly. Social media can be a powerful tool for both positive and negative patient experiences, and it must be monitored by healthcare organizations, particularly with negative comments.

Often, word of mouth takes the form of stories. Marketing WOM is when these stories (positive) are actively encouraged. A compelling healthcare story is an account of events in a patient's (or patient's family's) healthcare journey that provides a meaningful narrative of their service encounter. Many healthcare organizations now use patient stories in their marketing campaigns as an effective way to differentiate their organization and personalize the healthcare experience.

3 ORGANIZATIONS USING THE POWER OF PATIENTS IN HEALTHCARE MARKETING

BY ANNIE ZELM

All companies should be concerned about protecting the privacy of their customers, but for healthcare organizations, it's not just good business practice—it's the law.

It's understandable, then, that healthcare marketers might be reluctant to weave patient testimonials into the story they tell. Besides concerns about patient privacy, marketers might assume patients don't want to talk about their experiences, or it's too difficult to track down someone who will agree to be featured on camera.

When they're done right, however, patient stories are powerful. Healthcare marketers who make it easy for patients to share as they feel compelled to do so won't have to go out every so often in search of a patient willing to sign a photo release or be interviewed; *the stories will come to them naturally.*

Here's a look at three healthcare companies that have mastered patient-centered marketing and what your company can learn from them.

AKRON CHILDREN'S HOSPITAL

Born with spina bifida, Jordan Pollock has been in physical therapy since he's been an infant. Now that he's in school, he uses a dynamic stander to be more independent during recess and gym class, while his classmates are running freely. He loves tractors, riding his bike and playing with his baby sister, Gabriella. Jordan's story is one of dozens featured on the Akron Children's Hospital blog.

These are the kind of stories that melt your heart, and the hospital's website always has a steady stream of them. That's because they make it simple for anyone to submit

their story, along with photos and videos. Patients can give a short testimonial or write a more detailed blog post about their experiences.

Pro Tip: Keep the lines of communication open all year long. Healthcare is emotional, and people are more willing to share their experiences than you might think. By having a streamlined process for them to do so, you're empowering patients to speak directly to others—and become your best advocates.

MEDTRONIC

As soon as you visit the website for this medical device giant, you get a sense of the bigger picture. This company isn't about selling pacemakers or titanium implants; it's about helping people live longer, more fulfilling lives.

The stories are inspiring: There's Kobi, a surfer who thought he would never walk again after crashing headfirst into rocks and damaging his cervical vertebrae. There's Sharon, who was spared large scars after a mastectomy.

And there's Bruce, a former New York Jets football player who nearly died after suffering sudden cardiac arrest He went on to found a mentoring program that matches retired athletes with high school leaders after he received an implantable cardioverter defibrillator.

Medtronic even rewards patients for sharing their stories by offering them the opportunity to apply for a $20,000 charitable grant for using their "extra lives" to serve the greater good.

Pro Tip: Incentives can go a long way to encourage sharing and inspire others. They don't have to be large monetary rewards, either. It could be as simple as recognizing them at an annual awards banquet. Consider launching a program that honors patients who have gone on to do something remarkable.

MAYO CLINIC

Sometimes social media marketing *is* brain surgery. The Mayo Clinic's collection of awe-inspiring videos feature patients who play the violin during surgery and accomplish remarkable feats afterward.

The nation's best hospital has set a new standard for building a community, with more than half a million Facebook fans and more than 25,000 YouTube subscribers. Its posts are a mix of physician videos, patient perspectives, roundtable discussions, and live chats connecting patients with experts.

As a brand, it's so widely recognized that the interaction between its physicians and the public seems to happen naturally. Visitors arrive at the site searching for answers, and the Mayo Clinic's staff quickly responds with answers they can trust. Those questions then shape the Mayo Clinic's content marketing efforts, leading to explanatory videos, blog posts, and even real-time conversations. Behind those conversations is a team of experts and producers who facilitate them.

Pro Tip: It's hard to compete with the level of resources at an institution like the Mayo Clinic, but your company can still direct the conversation in your own way. If you're a hospital or physician's group, consider having a rotating panel of physicians who regularly post answers to patient questions or host a short interactive chat once a month. These short interactions can go a long way to build trust over time. The key is consistency.

Healthcare organizations have a tremendous responsibility to care for and protect their patients, but they also have a unique opportunity to share the kind of stories that really matter. They should look to patients who are already asking questions or sharing testimonials on their social media pages as potential brand advocates and allow the conversation to happen naturally.

READING 5.2

STORYTELLING AS A STRATEGIC INITIATIVE

OVERVIEW

There is a business imperative to move the needle on patient experience performance. While data are important to demonstrate that change is needed, when they are presented with context they are more powerful. Stories provide that context. A compelling care story engages, incentivizes, and can inspire employees to improve patient experience in a way that cannot be achieved through data alone.

Healthcare organizations across the country are leveraging the rich detail of patient comments, stories, and vignettes to inspire employees and clinicians throughout the enterprise. At Press Ganey's 2015 National Client Conference, the Institute for Innovation's Founding Executive Council convened to share practices and insights on leveraging storytelling as a strategic initiative. We are pleased to summarize and share these insights.

STORYTELLING PRACTICES

ADVENTIST HEALTH SYSTEM: TOP STORYTELLING AWARD ENCOURAGES SHARING AND HEALTHY COMPETITION

Adventist Health System's intranet story portal allows care team members to record stories of exceptional patient care. These stories provide inspiring content for hospital leaders to start their internal meetings and create some friendly competition among Adventist hospitals.

- Storytelling award. According to Pam Guler, Vice President Patient Experience and Chief Experience Officer, system hospitals enjoy vying for the top storytelling award granted at the organization's annual summit. At last year's summit, the award was given to the hospital with the most stories submitted through the portal. This year, the award focused on how hospitals are using stories. Every hospital's C-suite submitted an application describing how they are leveraging patient stories. The winning organization—chosen by Adventist's CEO—shared its comprehensive work with Schwartz Rounds. Another hospital described how it is sharing patient stories throughout the community. The greatest benefit of the award process is that it helps hospitals network and share their story practices.

- <u>Starting at the top.</u> Adventist's CEO personally leverages patient stories by sharing "Mission Moments," video-recorded patient stories that speak to how Adventist caregivers carry out the organization's mission every day. Guler says that having a CEO who believes in the importance of patient stories cascades down through all hospital leaders and to frontline staff. Sharing patient stories helps reinforce the organization's mission and commitment to exceptional care.

BAPTIST HEALTH SOUTH FLORIDA: STORYTELLING AT BOARD MEETINGS, LEADERSHIP DEVELOPMENT INSTITUTE

Baptist Health South Florida uses storytelling to add an emotional component to its patient experience data. Dr. Thinh Tran, Chief Medical and Quality Officer, Corporate Vice President, relates that any data presented at Board meetings are coupled with patient stories. Patient vignettes are also included whenever the system publishes data for an entity (e.g., hospital, outpatient clinic). In addition, a Baptist Health patient and his or her family members are always invited to the organization's annual Leadership Development Institute to represent the patient voice.

BRIGHAM AND WOMEN'S HOSPITAL: "LOVE STORY" VIDEOS

Brigham and Women's Hospital models its "Love Stories" project after the movie, "When Harry Met Sally." The organization creates internal videos of a physician and a patient seated side by side, sharing details about their relationship. Off camera, an interviewer asks the "couple" questions such as, "How did you meet?", "Did you have any doubts?" Dr. Tom Lee, Press Ganey's Chief Medical Officer, says the goal of each vignette is to show that the physician-patient relationship is indeed a loving, authentic relationship. The stories engage Brigham and Women's employees and clinicians, demonstrate the importance of relationship in healthcare, and complement the organization's use of patient experience data.

CAROLINAS HEALTH CARE SYSTEM: SMALL TEAM EXERCISES

Carolinas Health Care System convenes frontline teammates at meetings to explore the concept of preventing avoidable patient suffering. According to Connie Bonebrake, Senior Vice President at Carolinas, one storytelling exercise that has proven to be impactful is having teammates work in small groups to create a story in response to images that depict individuals in various stressful circumstances (e.g., bankruptcy, homelessness, multi-tasking mom). Every story created by various groups is unique, yet they have all captured the impact of stress and helped teammates recognize the impact of unresolved stress can have on them as teammates. One image depicts a man holding his head in his hands with mounds of paper in front of him. One frontline nurse told the story of the overwhelming stress experienced by a health care executive trying to manage competing organizational priorities. These types of responses provide effective segues into discussions around teammate wellness and resiliency as well as the prevention of avoidable patient suffering.

NORTHWELL (FORMERLY NORTH SHORE LIJ HEALTH SYSTEM): CONNECT TO ORIGINAL CAREER INSPIRATION

Sven Gierlinger, Chief Experience Officer at North Shore LIJ Health System, says, "Everyone has a story of why they got into health care in the first place." This includes executives who are often so focused on running the business that they forget the reason they chose a career in healthcare. North Shore LIJ uses the art of storytelling to help its executives connect back to their original inspiration. Executives attend a four-hour retreat that centers on the themes of empathy and connectedness. They are prompted to tell several types of stories, including the story of why they got into healthcare, as well as a story about giving or receiving empathy.

The stories are transformative. Executives who may not have been known for expressing themselves openly are frequently among the first to share their stories. Teams that have worked together for years often are unaware of why their colleagues got into healthcare. Knowing each other's stories is a powerful way to build meaningful connections.

North Shore LIJ also leverages the power of negative patient stories. For example, after a patient posted an unfavorable comment about the organization on a social media outlet, Gierlinger personally called the patient to hear about the experience. After listening to the story, he invited the patient to come in for an interview so that the story could be recorded. A video of the seven-minute interview was shown after lunch at a senior leader retreat as a contrast to a positive patient story that was shared before the lunch break. The contrast between the positive and negative patient care stories was so powerful that senior leaders still talk about it today with their teams.

UCLA HEALTH SYSTEM: BUILDING DIRECT CAREGIVER STORIES IN THEIR TIME AND SPACE

UCLA Health System incorporates storytelling by bringing stories of exceptional patient care directly to their caregivers. For example, they will gather a group of leaders together to go to the plastic surgery clinic, a nursing unit huddle, etc. and spend five minutes sharing a patient's story of how the care team made a difference. Tony Padilla, Director of Patient Affairs, says the organization strives to make these meetings convenient for direct caregivers by holding them "in their time, in their space, with their team." Padilla reflects that bringing patients themselves to these meetings may be a positive enhancement for the organization to consider.

UNIVERSITY OF CHICAGO MEDICINE: RECOGNIZE MOMENTS THAT MAKE A DIFFERENCE EVERY DAY

University of Chicago Medicine's "Making a Difference Every Day" program centers on the question, "How do we change a world?" and is designed to help employees and clinicians understand that they are surrounded by "change a world" moments with patients every day. According to Dr. Alison Tothy, Chief Experience and Engagement Officer, the goal is for every employee and clinician in the system—not only frontline staff—to learn to recognize these moments and to strive to make a difference in the lives of patients each day.

As a result of the program, stories of exceptional patient experiences surface frequently. The organization leverages these stories at their quarterly "Making a Difference Every Day Best Practices Forum." For the first year of the forum, the agenda was highly data driven. At the event, attendees heard about employees and clinicians who were recognized for providing great care, but not in the form of storytelling. Attendance began to wane. To revitalize the forums, the organization started incorporating patient stories into the agenda.

University of Chicago Medicine standardizes the process of identifying and developing the patient stories presented during the forums. The five-step process includes:

1. **Identifying Patients:** Exceptional patient experiences are identified through discharge care calls and patient survey comments.

2. **Interviewing Patients:** Patients and family members are interviewed about their experience to prepare them for the questions that will be asked during the forum.

3. **Identifying Care Teams:** During the pre-forum interview, patients identify members of their care team that they would like to join them on stage.

4. **Prepping Care Teams:** Care team members are prepared with the questions that will be asked of them during the forum.

5. **Promoting the Event:** The upcoming forum is advertised throughout the organization.

At the event, University of Chicago Medicine senior leadership delivers an opening address and introduces the patient and family members. The Patient Experience Leadership Team interviews the patient using a "talk show" format as an engaging way to help them share their story. Patients are asked questions such as, "Why did this work?" and "Why do you love your caregivers?" The interview then shifts focus toward the care team and how they worked together to create such an exceptional experience for the patient.

After the forum, certificates and thank-you cards are provided to the patient and family members. In some instances, patients are invited to become more active in the organization's activities. Some patients have joined University of Chicago Medicine's advisory boards, attended unit huddles, and participated in quality improvement initiatives such as operational experience mapping.

Forum attendance has increased since incorporating patient stories into the agenda. Challenges still exist, including getting more representation from frontline staff at the events. The organization is working through these challenges so that patient stories can reach more caregivers. For example, the forums are recorded and made available via the intranet so that segments of the event can be shared at department meetings.

University of Chicago Medicine's best practices forums are an emotional experience for both patients and caregivers. They give patients an opportunity to express heart-felt thanks to their care team. From the caregiver perspective, patient stories connect back to the Making a Difference Every Day mission and help remind them of why they chose a career in healthcare. To reinforce that reminder, the organization has created an inspiring video compilation of caregiver quotes and photos called "Remembering Why."

YALE-NEW HAVEN HOSPITAL: NARRATIVES AT MONTHLY SERVICE LINE PX FORUMS

Dr. Michael Bennick, Associate Chief of Medicine, Medical Director, Patient Experience, at Yale-New Haven Hospital, observes that "Data tend to blind and stories tend to engage." To that point, when Dr. Bennick opened Yale-New Haven's annual patient experience conference this year, he started with a slide showing a graphic of the organization's patient experience performance. He then had the slide fade into a compilation of patient and caregiver photos to emphasize that there are thousands of stories behind the data.

The organization recognizes some of these stories during service-line patient experience forums. On a monthly basis, every service line at Yale-New Haven holds a patient experience forum during which they share a story of exceptional patient care. The patients and families involved in the story attend the event as well to participate in the experience and to celebrate the care team.

Yale-New Haven has also implemented efforts designed to keep their patients' personal stories front and center, even at the bedside. For example, family members are encouraged to create a communication board that can be displayed in the patient's room depicting the patient's life and interests. The board tells the patient's story and helps caregivers to see the patient as a person, distinct from their medical condition.

The organization also believes in the power of the narrative. The author of *Cutting for Stone*, Abraham Verghese, was invited to discuss how to create a potent narrative.

In addition, the organization began training undergraduates to interview patients about their life stories using open-ended questioning techniques. After each patient is interviewed, the student writes the patient's story, gives it to the patient to review, and then laminates the story and gives it to the patient as a gift. The patient's story is also included in the "FYI" section of the electronic medical record.

CONCLUDING INSIGHTS

Storytelling can be a powerful motivator for change. For example, after hearing a patient story, Cleveland Clinic physicians were driven to institute a same-day appointment policy. The patient called the urology department with concerns and was told that there were no openings for two weeks. The patient ended up in the emergency department within hours of trying to schedule the appointment.

Storytelling can also be a powerful source of inspiration. Stories of exceptional care instill pride in the organization and illustrate what care should look like for every patient. They celebrate the hard work caregivers do every day to reduce patient suffering and serve as reminders of why they chose a career in health care in the first place. According to Dr. Lee, "What we're trying to do is make them better for the next patient they see and help them see themselves in a light that sustains them as they go about their work."

Patient stories engage: they contain character, conflict, and resolution—all elements that complement and enhance data. "When I go to get funding for a program, stories are great, but the first question we're asked is, 'Is it going to make a difference in the data?'" says Dr. Tothy. The combination of data and stories can make the most compelling business cases. John Bingham, Vice President, Performance Improvement and Chief Quality Officer at The University of Texas MD Anderson Cancer Center agrees, "Isn't it the best of both worlds when you can combine good data with good stories that link—it seems like that's where the sweet spot is."

UNDERSTANDING PATIENT LOYALTY

The following summaries of recent peer-reviewed studies and articles identify factors that influence patient loyalty and the likelihood to recommend an organization or care provider. **[PG]** denotes Press Ganey research.

EMERGENCY DEPARTMENT		
STUDY	OBJECTIVE	CONCLUSION
Guss, D. A., Gray, S., & Castillo, E. M. (2014). The impact of patient telephone call after discharge on likelihood to recommend in an academic emergency department. *The Journal of Emergency Medicine, 46*(4), 560–566.	To assess the impact of post-discharge telephone calls on emergency department patient satisfaction as measured by likelihood to recommend.	• Post-discharge phone calls are an effective strategy to improve emergency department patient satisfaction. • Post-discharge calls to emergency department patients are strongly associated with improved patient satisfaction as measured by likelihood to recommend. • The strong association between post-discharge calls and patient satisfaction remains after controlling for waiting time, total length of emergency department stay, and acuity (as assessed by triage class).
Johnson, M. B., Castillo, E. M., Harley, J., & Guss, D. A. (2012). Impact of patient and family communication in a pediatric emergency department on likelihood to recommend. *Pediatric Emergency Care, 28*(3), 243–246.	To Identify the specific emergency department patient experience variables that most strongly predict satisfaction as measured by likelihood to recommend.	• A strong correlation exists between nurse and physician communication and emergency department patients' likelihood to recommend. • Keeping the patient informed is the communication variable with the strongest correlation to patients' likelihood to recommend. • Increased daily census and increased median daily wait times have no impact on emergency department patients' likelihood to recommend.
Liu, S. S., Franz, D., Allen, M., Chang, E. C., Janowiak, D., Mayne, P., & White, R. (2010). ED services: The impact of caring behaviors on patient loyalty. *Journal of Emergency Nursing, 36*(5), 404–414.	To describe the impact of caring behaviors in the emergency department on patient loyalty.	• Caring behaviors—including care concern and communication, body language, and initial greetings—have an impact on patient loyalty. • Making sure patients are aware of care-related details, working with a caring touch, and making treatment procedures clearly understood are the caring behaviors most strongly correlated with patient loyalty. • Time-stamp data show a link between wait time and patent loyalty.

INPATIENT		
STUDY	**OBJECTIVE**	**CONCLUSION**
[PG] Kessler, D. P., & Mylod, D. (2011). Does patient satisfaction affect patient loyalty? *International Journal of Healthcare Quality Assurance, 24*(4), 266–273.	To investigate the relationship between patient satisfaction and the propensity to return (i.e., loyalty).	• Patient satisfaction affects hospital choice. There is a significant link between patient satisfaction and loyalty. • Patient satisfaction has business implications for healthcare providers and may be useful as a management tool for private and public purchasers.
Senti, J., & LeMire, S. D. (2011). Patient satisfaction with birthing center nursing care and factors associated with likelihood to recommend institution. *Journal of Nursing Care Quality, 26*(2), 178–185.	To determine which care factors are most important to birthing center patients and correlated with the likelihood to recommend the facility to others.	• Wait time, communication, and services in the hospital birthing center influence satisfaction with care and correlate with likelihood to recommend. • Wait time for call light response accounted for the largest amount of survey variability and was correlated with likelihood to recommend the facility.
MEDICAL PRACTICE		
STUDY	**OBJECTIVE**	**CONCLUSION**
Carlin, C. S. (2014). Patient loyalty in a mature IDS market: Is population health management worth it? *Health Services Research, 49*(3), 1011–1033.	To understand patient loyalty to providers in Integrated Delivery Systems (IDS) over time, informing effective population health management.	• Once the patient shows loyalty to a care system, his or her chance of switching relationships is very low in future years. • Co-located primary and specialty services are important in maintaining primary care loyalty. • Investment in population health management makes sense for both patient health and the financial health of a care system in a shared savings contract.
[PG] Press Ganey Associates, Inc. (2014). Protecting market share in the era of reform: Understanding patient loyalty in the medical practice segment. *Performance Insights.*	To identify the key determinants of patient loyalty for medical practices.	• The following variables are key determinants of patient loyalty for medical practices: - Confidence in the care provider - Coordination of care - Concern care providers show for patients' questions and worries - Listening - Courtesy of care providers • The most important predictor of patient loyalty is patients' confidence in their care providers.

MEDICAL PRACTICE (*continued*)		
STUDY	OBJECTIVE	CONCLUSION
Platonova, E. A., Kennedy, K. N., & Shewchuk, R. M. (2008). Understanding patient satisfaction, trust, and loyalty to primary care physicians. *Medical Care Research and Review, 65*(6), 696–712.	To develop and test a model reflecting a system of interrelations among patient loyalty, trust, and satisfaction as they are related to patients' intentions to stay with a primary care physician and recommend the physician to others.	• Patient trust and good interpersonal relationships with the primary care physician are major predictors of patient satisfaction and loyalty to the physician. • Patients need to trust the primary care physician to be satisfied and loyal to the physician. • Patient trust, satisfaction, and loyalty are strong and significant predictors of patients' intentions to stay with a primary care physician and to recommend the physician to others.
OUTPATIENT		
STUDY	OBJECTIVE	CONCLUSION
Boss, E. F., & Thompson, R. E. (2012). Patient satisfaction in otolaryngology: Can academic institutions compete? *Laryngoscope, 122*(5), 1000–1009.	To describe ambulatory otolaryngology patient satisfaction and examine the association of teaching status. The item "likelihood-to-recommend practice" was measured as an indicator of patient loyalty.	• Otolaryngology patients seen in teaching or academic settings are more likely to recommend their care provider and more likely to recommend the practice where they received care. • Items that most strongly correspond with loyalty are related to care provider communication and behavior.
[PG] Fulton, B. R., Malott, D. L., Jr., & Ayala, L. (2010). Award-winning outpatient service: Finding the common thread. *The Journal of Medical Practice Management, 25*(4), 202–206.	To offer a conceptual framework for understanding the effects of communication initiatives and how they relate to patients' likelihood to recommend the organization.	• The extent and quality of communication with the patient and among healthcare team members, both during and after the patient's visit, are key drivers of the patient's increased likelihood to recommend the organization. • Patients' satisfaction with their visit and post-visit requires effective and clear communication which will translate into adherence to medical guidelines and an improved quality of life. This, in turn, will impact the likelihood to recommend the organization, their experience of future visits to the organization, and whether or not to have a future visit.

REFLECTIONS ON THE READING SELECTIONS

We offer the following editorial commentary on the reading selections.

1. HIPAA privacy rules can make it difficult to use patient testimonials in marketing initiatives. Always seek the guidance of your organization's legal counsel prior to using patient names.

2. If your organization wants to create a paradigm shift to a patient-centered experience, a significant cultural change must occur within the organization. In particular, the change must begin with top management. It must be apparent to all employees that creating memorable experiences for patients and their families is a priority and should therefore also be rewarded.

3. Data such as HCAHPS results provide a useful benchmark for service encounters, but the richness of qualitative information from patients should not be ignored. The open-ended HCAHPS data is often not analyzed due to the time-intensive nature of performing that analysis, but this is where the "why" of the scores is most evident.

APPLICATION AND SYNTHESIS

"Storytelling is human. We learn through stories, and we use them to make sense of our lives. It's a natural extension to think that we could use stories to improve our health." —*Dr. Thomas K. Houston* (Chen, 2011)

QUESTIONS FOR DISCUSSION

1. Has a patient ever told you a story that had a profound impact on how you view healthcare?

2. What is your story—when and why did you choose a career in healthcare?

3. What can be done to encourage patients to tell their stories?

4. What in the current healthcare system makes it difficult for patients to tell their stories?

5. Are positive or negative stories more valuable to healthcare providers?

SUMMARY OF MAIN POINTS

After reading this chapter, you should be able to:

√ Discuss the meaning of a moment of truth (p. 156)
√ Identify the steps in the listening process (p. 156–157)
√ Explain the usefulness of WOM to a healthcare organization (p. 157)

COMPREHENSION ASSESSMENT

1. Why is the moment of truth so difficult to manage within healthcare organizations?

2. Which step in the listening process is typically most difficult for healthcare providers? Why do you think this is difficult for them?

3. What impact has social media had on WOM?

CONCLUSION

In this chapter, we discussed the importance of listening and understanding how moments of truth define the service encounter for patients and their families. Marketers can leverage patient stories of exceptional care in their promotional efforts, and these stories can motivate employees to deliver a memorable healthcare experience for their patients.

The next chapter will focus on managing the patient experience. We will provide examples of how caregivers focus on patient-centered healthcare experiences.

REFERENCES

Chen, P. W. (2011). *When patients share their stories, health may improve.* Retrieved from http://www.nytimes.com/2011/02/10/health/views/10chen.html?_r=0.

Henkel, R. J. & P. A. Maryland (2015). The risks and rewards of value-based reimbursement. *Frontiers of Health Services Management, 32*(2), 3–16.

Johnson, M. B., Castillo, E. M., Harley, J., & Guss, D. A. (2012). Impact of patient and family communication in a pediatric emergency department on likelihood to recommend. *Pediatric Emergency Care, 28*(3), 243–246.

Kessler, D. P. & Mylod, D. (2011). Does patient satisfaction affect patient loyalty? *International Journal of Healthcare Quality Assurance, 24*(4), 266–273.

Liu, S. S., Franz, D., Allen, M., Change, E. C., Janowiak, D., Mayne, P., & White, R. (2010). ED services: The impact of caring behaviors on patient loyalty. *Journal of Emergency Nursing, 36*(5), 404–414.

Press Ganey Associates, Inc. (2014). Protecting market share in the era of reform: Understanding patient loyalty in the medical practice segment. *Performance Insights.*

Study.com (2017). *The four stages of the listening process.* Retrieved from http://study.com/academy/lesson/the-four-stages-of-the-listening-process.html.

IMAGE CREDITS

6
CHAPTER

HOW CAREGIVERS CREATE VALUE

LEARNING OBJECTIVES

In this chapter, you will learn about the following:

- The differences between types of teams
- The advantages of teamwork in healthcare
- Characteristics of effective teams
- Challenges in creating effective teams in healthcare

INTRODUCTION

An essential component of creating value for patients is an effective team of health-care professionals. In this chapter, we will explore different types of teams and how to create effective teams in healthcare organizations.

NOTES FROM PRACTICE

Figure 6.1 Wow Image

HOSPITAL'S SERVICE EXCELLENCE PROGRAM AIMS TO "WOW" GUESTS

Wow! It's a three-letter exclamation that conveys a wide range of positive emotions—surprise, happiness, fun, delight, admiration, respect. It's that type of feeling that the East Texas Medical Center Regional Healthcare System based in Tyler, Texas, wanted all its guests to express about the care they receive there.

CREATING A CUSTOM-DESIGNED SERVICE EDUCATION EXPERIENCE

ETMC WOW!, the service program's name, was the culmination of a year's worth of education, planning, and hard work by a group of committed members of the ETMC team—more than 40 employees from a variety of areas at ETMC and from all levels within the organization. "We respect our employees and feel they're the best people to plan an effective service excellence program," Carroll Rogé, vice president of marketing and planning, explained. "So it was important to ask ETMC team members from throughout the hospital to offer input to provide as many different perspectives as possible."

Rogé facilitated the work of the ETMC WOW! service excellence committee. He began by conducting extensive research on how hospitals and other organizations improved the way they interact with their guests. He said, "When the leadership team asked me to look for ways to improve our service, the first step was to determine what the experts in customer service were saying." After attending seminars held by the Studer Group and the Disney Institute and reviewing scores of books and articles from many sources, Rogé shared what he had learned with the ETMC WOW! committee, which met each week for two hours over a period of six months.

"We knew that we didn't want to try to 'transplant' another program onto what we're doing here at ETMC," Rogé explained. Instead, the committee learned about a variety of approaches and then voted on the concepts they felt would be most helpful to improving service at ETMC. The goal was truly to identify the "best of the best" and bring those concepts to ETMC.

STRIVING TO CREATE A SENSE OF FUN

A concern of the committee was that employees might greet the program with a sense of skepticism or dread. "After all," Rogé said, "it's easy for staff members to hear about a new program and think that it's going to create a lot of extra work for them." He said nothing could be further from the truth, explaining that a consistent theme in all the customer service literature is that providing great guest services actually makes the work of employees easier. "When guests are happy, they're better patients," Rogé said. "They're more compliant. They feel more assured and confident in their care. They're just happier. And that makes the job of our caregivers that much easier."

Next, the committee considered how to bring the program to life. The word "wow" reminded the members of comic book exclamations like "pow!" and "bam!" So the group decided to adopt a superhero theme. "That's really not that much of a stretch," Rogé said. "The employees who provide direct patient care *are* viewed as heroes. They take care of our guests. They save lives. If health-care workers are viewed as heroes, then why shouldn't we strive to be 'super' heroes?"

BREAKING IT DOWN AND MAKING IT CLEAR

One of the Disney Institute's key points is that whatever guest relations approach is adopted, it must be clear and understandable to service providers, and they must know how to bring it to life. The first step, according to Disney, is creating the service theme. The service theme is an organizational pledge, a motto, or a mission statement that succinctly outlines how ETMC will be known for its commitment to guest relations.

The service theme represents the organization's focus on service. According to Disney, staff members also need service standards, which describe individual behaviors each employee must provide to bring the service theme to life.

1. I anticipate needs and exceed expectations by focusing on details!
2. I AM CONSISTENTLY POSITIVE AND ENGAGING!
3. I display KINDNESS, sensitivity, and respect to everyone!
4. I reach OUT TO MY GUESTS by USING "GREAT" COMMUNICATION!
5. I practice "fast" and effective service recovery!
6. I support and encourage my team members!
7. I maintain a clean and welcoming environment and personal appearance!

"The service theme and the service standards will serve as the core of the WOW! program," Rogé explained. From there, the committee developed a host of ongoing programs to reinforce these concepts and make them part of the culture at ETMC.

DEVELOPING A COMPREHENSIVE WOW! APPROACH

An elaborate, superhero-themed kickoff event was held for ETMC team members featuring games, great food, and prizes to explain the program and create excitement. Following the launch, the educational centerpiece of the ETMC WOW! program was a day-long educational program designed to instill the importance of all aspects of guest services to all 7,000 ETMC team members. An additional ETMC WOW! training session for managers was held as well. Yearly follow-up training is also held to reinforce ETMC WOW! principles.

"The education was fun and lively," Rogé said. "People learn better when they're having a good time." To that end, Rogé and his in-house marketing team animated the program's icons, Captain WOW! and WOW! Girl, allowing them to interact with the facilitators during the training presentation." Rogé said, "We created the illusion that we were actually conversing with these heroic program icons. This allowed us to keep everyone's attention by having fun and providing entertainment to facilitate learning."

The training also includes educational videos shot using actual ETMC employees in service situations that sparked discussion and dialogue. During the training, the team members in attendance work in small groups to solve service dilemmas and report back to the larger group. Again, this interactive learning helps everyone internalize the concepts to facilitate learning. The program

Figure 6.2a Wow Superhero   Figure 6.2b Wow Superhero

includes an employee reward and recognition component, special resources to help employees recover effectively when customers have been disappointed, an intranet resource site, and various opportunities for guests and employees to suggest customer service improvements. A facility walk-through system to improve the service setting was also implemented. A variety of promotional means, such as posters, flyers, and ongoing newsletter features, continue the process of educating staff on the importance of ETMC WOW! concepts. Results of various guest satisfaction monitoring surveys are reviewed regularly to ensure that ETMC WOW! is continuing to achieve its goals.

TEAMWORK

As we have discussed in previous chapters, the patient and their family encounter many "touch points" throughout their healthcare experience. The complexity of the service encounter requires that every employee participate as part of a team—each contributing to and enhancing the quality of the patient experience.

Teamwork is defined as a group that is working together toward a common goal or outcome. There is usually some form of relationship between the members (i.e., role responsibilities, development of trust). *Collaboration* is different from teamwork—it can take place even if the participants do not consider themselves as part of the team.

Within healthcare, an effective team is defined by the World Health Organization (WHO) as "one where the team members, including the patient, communicate with one another, as well as combining their observations, expertise, and decision-making responsibilities to optimize care. There is some evidence that multidisciplinary teams improve the quality of services and lower costs. Good teamwork has also been shown to reduce errors and improve care for patients, particularly those with chronic illnesses. In addition, understanding the culture of their workplace and its impact on team dynamics and functioning will make an individual a good team player."

Figure 6.3 Teams Should Span the Entire Organization

Figure 6.4 Should the Patient be Part of the Team?

The WHO also provides insight into characteristics of successful teams: "There are many models to describe effective teamwork. Historically, these have come from other industries, such as the aviation's crew resource management (CRM). CRM was developed by the aviation industry to improve communication in the cockpit and implement team-centered decision-making systems. CRM is defined as 'using all available sources—information, equipment, and people—to achieve safe and efficient flight operations.' CRM has been used in healthcare to improve teamwork and communication and initiate other safe processes."

The characteristics of CRM include a common purpose, measurable goals, effective leadership, good cohesion, and mutual respect. Other requirements include a proficiency of technical and teamwork skills, task motivation, flexibility, the ability to monitor their own performance, effective resolution of and learning from conflict, and engagement in situation monitoring (WHO).

READING SELECTION

READING 6.1

TEAMWORK AND PERFORMANCE

BY PHIL GLANFIELD

INTRODUCTION

CASE STUDY: AN EVERYDAY STORY OF TEAMWORK

Sharon is an orthopaedic consultant at an English hospital. There she has three operating sessions each week and sees ambulatory patients in an outpatient clinic. Clinically she is particularly interested in non-invasive techniques and pain control. Some of her colleagues come to her for advice on these issues, others don't. It seems to her that a number of practices in the orthopaedic department are out of date. Most of the time Sharon enjoys her work; some days are better than others. Tuesday and Friday are usually good days when the theatre sessions always seem to go well.

Sharon is concerned about the number of referrals she is receiving from general practitioners—are they all necessary? Sometimes it is difficult to make a decision based on the limited information in the referral letter. There isn't enough time to see everybody and it is difficult to get hold of the GP. She wonders what happens at the other nearby hospitals.

The hospital has recently been downgraded within the government's annual performance rating system. Last year it was classified as a high performing hospital. This year it has been downgraded to a rating of "poor performing" because of its financial performance and waiting times in the Accident and Emergency Department (A&E). Sharon hasn't noticed any significant difference in the hospital before or since the rating was announced. She knows there are problems in A&E because they are always looking for beds. Her clinical colleagues at a neighbouring hospital joke with her about being a "poor performing doctor." She doesn't think that is funny!

Sharon's story will help us to explore contemporary teamwork in this chapter. She and we know when we are working in a good team because even the most challenging of tasks is enjoyable, we have a sense of purpose, and of being in this together. We are learning on the job and we all take pride in the results that we see. And, uncomfortable as it is, we must also acknowledge that close-knit teams are capable of getting things badly wrong while being convinced that they are doing a good job. This happens in the boardroom (Enron) and on the frontline of care (Argyris 1990).

So what is the relationship between teamwork and performance improvement. What does teamwork mean in today's complex and ever-changing world? How can we create the kind of teams that we would aspire to work in and that gets great results?

SERVICE DELIVERY, TEAMS, AND WORKING LIFE

Teamwork in contemporary working life calls into question some of the traditional ways of thinking about teams and organising. The very word "team" conjures up a picture of a small group of people who work alongside each other and are engaged in a common task with a common purpose. And yet, as Sharon illustrates, we often belong to a number of teams simultaneously: Sharon moves in and out of different teams in the same day, from the theatre to the ward to a multidisciplinary case conference. Team or workgroup, membership is often temporary:[1] rotas change, people come and go, new people join because of a new task or a reorganisation. Changes may be due to training requirements for clinical staff and career development for managers but not everybody moves. Sharon has been a consultant for five years and is beginning to find the turnover of managerial staff frustrating. She seems to keep going over the same ground with different people.

Paradoxically, interest in effective teamwork has increased in parallel with our interest in individual, professional accountability (O'Neill 2002). This can be a significant stumbling block in the development of multidisciplinary teams (Savage and Moore 2004). It is important to hold onto this as a paradox, not something to be resolved in favour of the individual or the team: both are vital. Effective multi-disciplinary teams provide better patient care (Zwarenstein and Bryant 2000) and individual professional accountability for patient care is inescapable.

Sometimes the team is invisible to the patient who sees only individual care providers in a sequence of encounters. Poor communication may become obvious to the patient if relevant information does not move as fast as they do. But the results of good, effective teamwork are likely to be the product of many interacting factors and may be unacknowledged and taken for granted. The team may be virtual in high- or low-tech ways. For example, telemedicine can be an effective way of making scarce resources and skills go further and email and phone conferences may be the most efficient way of swapping and creating information and intelligence. Even in circumstances where the team does not meet, as patients, we would want the group of people involved in our care to work together "as if they were a high performing team."[2]

Of course this begs the question of what constitutes high performance. The hospital that Sharon works in has been rated as poor performing on its past year's performance on some very specific indicators. What does that say about the whole organisation? More importantly what does past performance tell us about the capacity of the organisation and the teams within it to improve?

WE HAVE A PROBLEM!

The multifaceted nature of today's teamwork presents us with a problem with our traditional notion of teambuilding. Typically we think of team development as a linear process that happens over time: "storming, forming, norming, performing" (Tuckman 1965). In addition we pay attention to the psychological profiles and preferred behavioural style of individual team members and the team as a whole (for instance Belbin 2003). There is an underlying assumption of a balanced team with the *right* amount of the various ingredients or styles. Many organisations invest in teambuilding activities which are intended to accelerate the process of team development and bond the team together. Often these activities are "off the job" and even outdoors with a tenuous connection to the task at work. We draw parallels with sporting teams which may not be appropriate and exclude from the conversation those who are not interested in sport. Sharon prefers the arts and is bored by endless talk of golf!

In a healthcare setting, there are unlikely to be any circumstances in which team performance is as easy to measure as a sporting team and there are other awkward questions. What happens if workgroups are not static in their membership, if one person is not able to pick a team from scratch with the "right" profile? What happens if we can't get the team together or we can't afford to spend regular teambuilding time with each of our several teams? What if we don't have time to wait for the team to go through its stages of development?

TEAMWORK AND BEST PRACTICE

There is an interesting tension inherent in writing a chapter about teamwork in a book which draws heavily on quality improvement methodology which is rooted in a rational, scientific paradigm. In the scientific paradigm cause and effect can be established by breaking things down into their component parts and quantifying their impact. Once the causal connection has been isolated, then we can predict and measure the impact of changes and plan and control to achieve the desired outcome. This engineering perspective on the world has served us well through the industrial revolution, the growth of technology and the development of medical science. Through fundamental research, application development, trial and error, medical science has created powerful and effective diagnostic and therapeutic interventions so that in many circumstances we know what constitutes best practice. We call this an evidence base. This way of thinking about how we understand the world in which we live has become so dominant that it goes unquestioned and has become universally applicable; it informs orthodox ideas about teams and teambuilding. This leads us to understand teams by breaking them into their component psychological parts and to accelerate development through linear, diagnostic, and therapeutic processes. We expect to be able to plan and manage teams based on some evidence about best practice.

The problems with the application of scientific thinking to a social context are well illustrated through the example of implementing evidence-based medicine. Typically, evidence based medicine is understood as "a body of evidence, separated from its social context, that can be unilaterally transmitted from the research setting—where it is known—to the world of practice—where it is not" (Wood *et al.* 1998:1730). Usually the locus is on the production of high quality knowledge that "speaks for itself;" theory (evidence) is isolated, proved, and must therefore be used. Where there is attention paid to implementation the discussion is normative, linear, or "top down" in tone, using the language of "planned change." The use of incentive structures is also proposed to promote compliance. There is a search for effective interventions and change levers such as the development of educational programmes. Local change champions should be informed and motivated to implement desired change.

(Ferlie *et al.* 2000:97)

Sometimes there is recognition that the evidence does not speak for itself, something else is needed to achieve a change in practice. Change needs to be *engineered* through a variety of *mechanisms*. So the paradigm that developed the evidence also informs the approach to implementation. However, numerous studies have shown a modest relationship between scientific evidence base and clinical behaviour change. "This confirms the long-established proposition that 'science-push' is by itself a weak influence on behaviour" (Ferlie *et al.* 2000:97). Ferlie also concludes that "the micro politics and capacity of the local clinical group as a whole also determine rates of local learning and change" (Ferlie *et al.* 2000:101). This underlines the importance of the team and workgroup to effective practice. Arguably the most important characteristic of a team is that the individuals learn from and with each other as they go about their task.

LEARNING AND INTERDEPENDENCE

Stacey (2003) takes up this theme in his description of learning as an activity of interdependent people and begins to shape a different understanding of team. Earlier we touched on the question of individual professional autonomy and teamwork. Often this is posited as a dilemma that must be resolved in favour of the team or the individual; which is the superior authority? Stacey (2003) frames such situations differently, as a paradox; "a state in which two diametrically opposing forces/ideas are simultaneously present, neither of which can ever be resolved or eliminated." For the clinician, accountability to her or his profession and, at the same time, accountability to the local team or organisation is an everyday reality. Providing health services is complex and complicated; different professions have different perspectives and make different contributions. Physicians and surgeons will often see the world differently and teams operating at the interface of healthcare and social care are likely to take a different perspective again.

From the patient's perspective, each and every contribution is important and it is equally important for each contribution to be provided in a timely way. In other words, healthcare is a highly interdependent activity in which all the actors are codependent. Any change or improvement in one area has implications for the whole. Innovative practice emerges from day to day conversations as staff grapple with the exigencies of a particular patient's condition and circumstances. And this is not planned in the sense of working to a blueprint or master plan. No one individual can be said to be "in control" in the sense that others follow their orders, rather "widespread coherent, evolving patterns emerge from local interaction" (Stacey 2003). Often difference in a workgroup or team is seen as a problem, but here difference, paradox, conflict is valued because the interaction of those differences gives rise to new patterns, new and better ways of providing a service.

> This view of organisation focuses attention on the way in which ordinary everyday conversations between people are perpetually creating the future, in the present, in the form of shifting patterns of communication and power relations. What is being perpetually created is nothing other than inseparable individual and collective identities.

> (Stacey 2003:8)

CASE STUDY

Sharon looks at her email and marvels at the latest management speak from the Human Resources Director. What can he mean? She is glad to be distracted by Sam, another orthopaedic specialist who she likes but sees as a bit of a stick in the mud as he has worked in the same way for years. He jokes: "At your email again, shouldn't you be seeing patients? We've got performance targets to hit!" It dawns on Sharon that this is the chance she has been waiting for, "Actually I am," she says, "I'm answering queries from general practitioners and physiotherapists about possible patient referrals." Sharon goes on to describe a project she has been involved in with primary care clinicians and the two hospitals,

> I offered to use my practice to test out potential improvements. To start with, we collated the available data about each step of the patient journey, from end to end, and developed a way of reporting this information routinely so everyone could see what was happening. We called it our "dashboard." The information revealed that some issues I thought were problematic, quality of referral and referral letters, were working well, but improvements could be made in other areas by redirecting referrals to a physiotherapist and better

selection of diagnostic tests. We have set up an electronic discussion forum so that primary care clinicians can discuss potential referrals with me. They email and I respond each day at a time that suits me. The results have been encouraging: patients in most pain are seen more quickly, other patients are treated earlier avoiding the need for surgery, I need fewer outpatient sessions because fewer patients are directly referred to me so I am able to spend more time in theatre. I think we should do this across the orthopaedic team.

SO WHAT?

If we take the interdependent, co-created clinical activity that we see in Sharon's work as our starting point (rather than an abstract notion of teamwork), then we can begin to explore what it might mean for our understanding of and approach to teams. In the case study, we have looked at only a small part of Sharon's working day and yet it is apparent that she works in a number of different teams that have different tasks and characteristics. We might think of these different examples as:

- *Physical teamwork:* when Sharon turns up for a theatre session her team does not have to discuss what they are going to do and who is going to do it; everyone knows their job and they get on with it. On Tuesdays and Fridays it is usually the same anaesthetist and most of the team have been together for some time so they have got to know each other well. Things "just happen," often there is no need to talk, but there is always time for a chat.
- *Virtual teamwork:* the project team that Sharon was part of met a few times as a small group but the project itself covers lots of people in different locations. It would be hard, if not impossible, to identify everyone who was affected by it. Sharon has met some of the people she "meets" in the electronic referral forum but by no means all—and it doesn't seem to matter.
- *Distributed teamwork:* some teams seldom get together, if at all, and yet they develop a strong sense of shared values, belonging, and working practice.

CONCLUSION

This chapter has sought to demonstrate that there is an important relationship between teamwork and high performance and that the pattern of teamwork often changes frequently as we move through the working day. In seeking to improve team performance, therefore, we need to pay attention to the task and the demands that the task places on the interrelationship of team members. In shaping our approach, we need to take into account the pre-existing quality of the local relationships (social capital) and we should pay at least as much attention to the quality of a team as we do to its quantifiable performance.

1. How does the multifaceted nature of today's teamwork influence working on performance improvement?

2. How could we determine the quality requirements of a team according to the nature of a team?

3. How could we "just know" when we are part of a good team?

4. What role could leadership play in developing a team?

5. What factors do we need to take into account when giving feedback on outcomes to a team?

NOTES

1. For the purposes of this chapter, we regard the terms team and workgroup as synonymous.

2. Some research suggests that physical proximity does not automatically generate teamworking and may be detrimental.

3. Reg Revans (1998) draws an important distinction between answerable puzzles, where the task is to find the answer, and problems with no known or agreed solution.

REFERENCES

Argyris, C. (1990) *Overcoming organisational defenses.* Boston, MA: Allyn & Bacon.

Belbin, M. (2003) *Management teams: why they succeed or fail.* Oxford and Boston, MA: Butterworth Heinemann.

Critehley B. and Casey, D. (1984) Second thoughts on team building. *Management Education and Development,* 15(2): 163–175.

Ferlie, E., Fitzgerald, L. and Wood, M. (2000) Getting evidence into clinical practice: an organisational behaviour perspective. *Journal of Health services Research and Policy.* 5(2): 92–102.

Gergen, K. (1999) *An invitation to social construction.* London: Sage.

Glanfield, P., Bevington, Anderson-Wallace, M. and Appleton, L. (2004) Getting to the heart of the matter. *In View,* 4 (December).

Goddard, M. Mannion, R. and Smith, P. (1999) Assessing the performance of NHS hospital trusts: the role of 'hard' and 'soil' information. *Health Policy,* 48: 119–134.

Kauffmann, S. (1993) *The origins of order: self organisation and selection in evolution.* New York: Oxford University Press.

Mayo, A. (2001) *The human value of the enterprise.* London: Nicholas Brearley.

O'Neill, O. (2002) *A question of trust: the BBC Reith Lectures 2002.* Cambridge: Cambridge University Press.

Revans, R. (1998) *The ABC of action learning.* London: Lemos and Crane.

Savage, J. and Moore, L. (2004) *Interpreting accountability: an ethnographic study of practice nurses, accountability and multidisciplinary team decision making in the context of clinical governance.* London: Royal College of Nursing.

Shaw, P. (2002) *Changing conversations in organisations.* London: Routledge.

Stacey, R, (2003) Learning as an activity of interdependent people. *The Learning Organization.* 10(6): 325–331.

Stacey R., Griffen, D., and Shaw, P. (2000) *Complexity and management: fad or radical challenge to systems thinking.* London: Routledge.

Tuckman, B. (1965) Development sequence in small groups. *Psychological Bulletin,* 63: 349–399.

Walshe, K., and Higgins, J. (2002) The use and impact of inquiries in the NHS. *British Medical Journal,* 325:895–900.

Walshe, K., Harvey, G., Hyde, P. and Pandit, N.R. (2004) Organisational failure and turnaround: lessons for public services from the for-profit sector. *Public Money and Management,* special issue on public sector turnaround. 24(4): 201–208.

Wood, M., Ferlie, E. and Fitzgerald, L. (1998) Achieving clinical behaviour change: a case of being indeterminate. *Social Sciences and Medicine,* 47(11): 1720–1738.

Zwarenstein, M. and Bryant, W. (2000) Interventions to promote collaboration between nurses and doctors. *The Cochrane Database of Systematic Reviews,* Chichester: John Wiley.

REFLECTIONS ON THE READING SELECTION

We offer the following editorial commentary on the reading selection.

1. Although the healthcare setting for the case study of "Sharon" is an English hospital, the concerns and issues are relevant for hospitals in the U.S. as well.

2. As noted on p. 183, in many cases the presence of "teams" is unknown to the patient. A patient's assessment of the quality of their service encounter may only be tied to the provider that they see on a regular basis and not the entirety of the team.

APPLICATION AND SYNTHESIS

"Teamwork is the ability to work together toward a common vision. The ability to direct individual accomplishments toward organizational objectives. It is the fuel that allows common people to attain uncommon results." —*Andrew Carnegie* (www.goodreads.com)

QUESTIONS FOR DISCUSSION

1. What type of team (physical, virtual, or distributed) are you most familiar and comfortable with and why?

2. What does effective teamwork mean to you?

3. What role can teamwork play in creating the patient experience? Be concrete in your answer.

4. The World Health Organization says effective teamwork can have an immediate and positive impact on patient safety, and the importance of teams is increasing as medicine becomes more complex. Based on your own work experience, think of an example where effective teamwork could have or did make a difference. If your example was positive, how could you replicate it in the same or different circumstances?

5. What are some of the challenges healthcare professionals face in creating effective teams?

6. Is the patient part of the team? Why or why not, and how does the inclusion or exclusion impact the patient experience and compliance?

SUMMARY OF MAIN POINTS

After reading this chapter, you should be able to:

√ Discuss the aspects of an effective team (p. 179-181)
√ Explain how teamwork can be used within a healthcare organization to improve the patient experience (p. 181-190)

COMPREHENSION ASSESSMENT

1. How did the aviation industry impact teamwork in healthcare organizations?

2. What impact did the WHO say that teamwork has on quality patient care?

3. Identify how physical, virtual, and distributed teamwork are different.

CONCLUSION

In this chapter, we discussed the importance of teamwork in providing quality patient care. Although the nature of healthcare delivery is complex with multiple provider "touch points," a cohesive team is critical in ensuring quality care and optimal outcomes.

In the next chapter, we will discuss how an organization can create the patient-centric focus for success.

REFERENCES

Goodreads.com (2017). Retrieved from http://www.goodreads.com/quotes/ 251192-teamwork-is-the-ability-to-work-together-toward-a-common.

World Health Organization (2012). *Being an effective team player*. Retrieved from http://www.who.int/patientsafety/education/curriculum/course4_handout.pdf.

IMAGE CREDITS

7

CHAPTER

BEING PATIENT-CENTERED—A KEY FOR SUCCESS

LEARNING OBJECTIVES

In this chapter, you will learn about the following:

- What it means to have patient-centered care
- Patient satisfaction
- Defining the patient experience
- Applying best practices from other industries to healthcare
- HCAHPS scores regarding staff behaviors and the patient experience

INTRODUCTION

The nature of the healthcare environment is typically one in which the patient seeks medical care for either an acute or chronic problem. Healthcare providers focus on solving the patient's medical problems in the most efficient way possible. However, if we seek to create a memorable healthcare experience for the patient and their family members, we must begin to approach the service encounter differently. Walt Disney believed in creating magic for each guest who visited his theme park. Each member of the Disney team was responsible for making the visit magical and memorable. In this chapter, we will explore other industries to discover innovative approaches to providing a patient-centered experience.

NOTES FROM PRACTICE

Figure 7.1 Patrick
Simonson

THE TUCKER ADVISORY GROUP, INC.

"ACHIEVING SUCCESS THROUGH PERFORMANCE"

PATRICK C. SIMONSON, MHSA, FACHE

DIRECTOR & SENIOR PROJECT EXECUTIVE

psimonson@ttag-inc.com   (215) 260–6102

Patrick Simonson has extensive experience in primary care and specialty practice management, project and service line leadership, business development, and interim executive roles with health systems, provider and community organizations. Recognizing the need for principle-centered leadership and attention to strategic and tactical imperatives, Patrick ensures effective project structure, client-driven approaches, and achievable work plans. He uses collaborative, facilitative, results-oriented methods to ensure team success and fulfillment.

Simonson's professional roles include, but are not limited to, 25 years of progressive management experience in corporate and health system organizations with an emphasis on launching and leading profitable ventures and achieving significant operations improvements and desired programmatic results. He is adept at transformation, balancing mission and margin metrics, ensuring positive patient experiences, and working well independently and with teams while being recognized for a unique ability to manage complexity and communicate effectively.

Simonson completed 11 interim leader roles and 34 consulting projects:

- Vice President of eight hospital-based practices at CHRISTUS Trinity Mother Frances
- Executive Director, Pinnacle Cardiovascular Institute

- COO: Blair Gastro Associates, Bux-Mont Oncology, Vet Referral Center
- Executive Director, Business Development and Physician Practices, Easton/CHS
- Project Executive Solutions for Management and The Tucker Advisory Group
- Director, Clinical Practice Group, Drexel University School of Medicine
- Director, Health Ventures Group, Lehigh Valley Health Network
- Regional Operations Manager, Cerner, and Client Executive, IBM Health Industry

Simonson earned a BS in social sciences from Indiana University of Pennsylvania and a Masters in health services administration from George Washington University. He holds a Healthcare Market Analysis and Practice Management certificates from the Wharton School at the University of Pennsylvania and graduated from the IBM Leadership and Advanced Management Institute. Patrick is on the faculty of DeSales University's healthcare MBA program and the management faculty at Cedar Crest College.

Simonson has served as president of the East Texas Chapter and on the board of the East Pennsylvania Health Executive Network for the American College of Healthcare Executives (ACHE) and is active in Pennsylvania MGMA. He serves as president of the St. Joseph the Worker School Board, president of the Comets Youth Sports Foundation, and is a member of two national ACHE teams focused on member success initiatives.

PATIENT-CENTERED CARE

The National Institutes of Health (NIH) defines patient-centered care as "health care that establishes a partnership among practitioners, patients, and their families (when appropriate) to ensure that decisions respect patients' wants, needs, and preferences and solicit patients' input on the education and support they need to make decisions" (Lee Scher, 2012). Although this is primarily focused around the patient-centered medical home (PCMH), it does shift the role of the patient to a more involved participant in their medical decisions.

PATIENT SATISFACTION

Patient satisfaction is the patient's perception, positive or negative, of the care they received in relation to their expectations of what they would receive. Patient satisfaction has been shown to have a positive impact on clinical outcomes and patient retention and to lower medical malpractice claims. Patient satisfaction has also been used as a proxy to measure the success of healthcare providers with the HCAHPS scores, although it does not directly measure patient satisfaction.

I misplaced my stethoscope warmer upper.

Figure 7.2 Many Small Things Create the Experience

THE PATIENT EXPERIENCE

The *patient experience* is the patient's perception of their healthcare journey with the provider. It begins with the patient's first realization that healthcare services are needed and includes all of the interactions with the provider and provider organization

Figure 7.3 Patient Perceptions are the Reality

until the healthcare issue is resolved. The patient's perception of the experience is shaped both by their emotions (subjective) and evaluation of the clinical outcomes (objective). A patient may have a positive clinical outcome and still have a negative patient experience; likewise, a patient may have a negative clinical outcome and still believe it was a positive experience. The objective and subjective portions of healthcare cannot be removed from the experience—experience is an overarching evaluation of both subjective and objective.

If you have ever talked with someone about their cruise vacation, you were probably told about the extensive food buffets and the animal-shaped towels on their bed. When someone purchases a cruise vacation, the primary service offering is the water transportation to a specific location. However, that is not the sole reason why individuals select cruises for their transportation needs. People select cruises because of the supplementary amenities that make the experience memorable, including how their assigned waiter might know their names and their specific drink and food requests. As we move toward creating better patient experiences, we should consider the supplementary amenities that might be appropriate to enhance the service encounter for patients and their family members.

Figure 7.4 Focusing on the Cruise Experience

READING SELECTIONS

READING 7.1

THE TRUTH ABOUT PATIENT EXPERIENCE: WHAT WE CAN LEARN FROM OTHER INDUSTRIES, AND HOW THREE *PS* CAN IMPROVE HEALTH OUTCOMES, STRENGTHEN BRANDS, AND DELIGHT CUSTOMERS

BY BRIAN R. NEEDHAM

EXECUTIVE SUMMARY

Improving the patient experience is an issue many healthcare organizations face. However, it is the opinion of this author that the focus on patient satisfaction scores alone is short-sighted and that the most successful organizations will adopt best practices from other industries to deliver a more complete patient experience. This article presents an extensive review of best practices in customer experience from numerous customer-centric industries and postulates as to how the healthcare field might apply them. A new framework for improving patient experience is proposed—one that moves beyond the traditional focus on satisfaction scores to embrace the core differentiating characteristics of the organization.

INTRODUCTION

Hospitals across the United States are working hard to figure out the key to delivering a superior patient experience. From 2000 to 2009, more than 400 articles were published on the subject, compared to fewer than 20 in the previous decade (Lecroy 2010). This number is expected to grow as patients become more selective and payers link reimbursement to patient satisfaction scores. Also, high patient satisfaction results in lower malpractice rates, better outcomes, more satisfied employees, and higher profitability than low patient satisfaction does (Aligning Forces for Quality 2010; Hall 2008). But many hospitals realize that patient experience is by no means easy to define, much less measure. A wealth of customer experience knowledge is available in other industries, yet healthcare has been slow to adopt these best practices. Now more than ever, healthcare organizations need to abandon their antiquated focus on services, satisfaction, and transactions in favor of attention to customers, loyalty, and relationships.

ORGANIZING AROUND CUSTOMERS

Healthcare organizations must stop trying to attract customers to their services and instead build services around customer needs. Progressive firms in other fields have already replaced or supplemented their chief marketing officer with a chief customer officer (CCO) or even a chief experience officer (often abbreviated as CXO)—in 2003 there were 30 CCOs; in 2010 there were more than 300 (Rust, Moorman, and Bhalla 2010; Cleveland Clinic 2010)—representing a major change in organizational structure. One reason hospitals and health systems are making the shift is the realization that a focus on customer needs may reveal preferences that customer surveys cannot show. Henry Ford's observation of the consumers' need for fast and reliable transportation led him to design the first car. He famously noted that had he instead asked consumers what they wanted, they would have likely replied, "Give us faster horses" (Meyer and Schwager 2007).

This anecdote exposes one primary flaw with market research today: Customers may not know what they want if their expectations are limited by previous experiences. Surveys show that healthcare consumers want more communication and coordination between their providers. However, an even better solution would be to have only one provider for all healthcare needs, thus eliminating the need for effective communication and coordination (Lathrop 1993). Other industries, such as real estate, have already made this transition. JLL, a real estate corporation with three main business units, created an umbrella group that serves as the main point of contact for important customers (Gulati 2007). Customer-focused actions such as these are supported by research in behavioral science that suggests the importance of addressing all the customer's needs in one transaction through one person (Freeman and Toman 2010).

However, healthcare organizations need to go beyond developing frontline staff with a breadth of knowledge to handle eclectic requests. They also need depth in handling the particular customer type that typically makes such requests. These "T-shaped" employees are rare and often must be trained, but they help organizations create patient-facing segments based on customer needs as opposed to product or service

BEING PATIENT-CENTERED—A KEY FOR SUCCESS | 201

offerings (Gulati 2007). Grote, Newman, and Sutaria (2007) found five suitable segments for commercially insured and Medicare patients:

- Comfort seekers
- Amenity seekers
- Control seekers
- Just the basics
- Physician reliant

Some companies such as General Electric appoint "customer champions," high-level executives who act as advocates for their customer segment (Gulati 2007).

By focusing on these customer segments, organizations can shift attention from current sales to lifetime value for consumers. While structuring operations around current sales can often lead to business myopia and perverse incentives, structuring them around consumers' lifetime value supports a customer-centric culture and long-term success. Keeping a customer satisfied and loyal has obvious benefits. Unsatisfied customers are more than twice as likely as satisfied customers to share their experience with ten or more people (Chase and Dasu 2001). In a world where the average adult with a social networking profile has 123 online friends, most of whose opinions they trust, customers are increasingly becoming a company's marketing department whether they like it or not (Mintel 2010; Reichheld 2003).

Intuit uses an innovative method to ensure customer needs are met. Rather than holding brainstorming sessions around new product designs, they hold "painstorming" sessions around customer frustrations with current products. Teams observe their target customers in their daily operations and note where customers are "pained." For example, farmers in India were unable to control demand for their produce, and as a result, many vegetables rotted or sold below value. Intuit staff painstormed around this issue, and within a few weeks they developed and launched beta testing of a mobile platform designed to harness demand, solving the farmers' problem (Martin 2011).

BUILDING LOYALTY

For years it was thought that satisfied customers will keep coming back to the company. However, the latest research shows that even the most satisfied customers may defect while the least satisfied may remain loyal, and some companies that successfully improve their customer satisfaction scores still see declines in profitability and growth (Freeman and Toman 2010). In competitive marketplaces, satisfaction with products and services is easy to come by. In fact, the national average for hospital patient satisfaction scores is close to 90 percent (Press Ganey 2011). But patients may still defect to other providers. Clearly, satisfaction is not the key to loyalty.

What, then, is the key to driving growth and loyalty? Many companies rely on the net promoter score, a calculation based on one question that asks customers their likelihood of recommending their company to a family member or friend (Reichheld 2003). By focusing on this one number, which is proven to be a strong predictor of growth in most industries, companies can provide faster turnaround times for performance analysis and thus adapt to customers' evolving needs more quickly.

Hence the focus shifts to what turns someone into a promoter. In 2010, Freeman and Toman provided insight by revealing that loyalty faces diminishing returns after companies achieve a certain level of satisfaction. In other words, healthcare organizations need only deliver the minimally accepted level of satisfying experiences; the rest of their resources should be devoted to removing obstacles for the customer to fulfill his or her request. The customer effort score (CES), an index that shows how much effort a customer personally needs to exert in solving his or her problem, is a strong predictor of customer loyalty (Freeman and Toman 2010).

FOCUSING ON RELATIONSHIPS

One flaw of the CES is that it does not take the whole patient experience into consideration. For years, management's approach to improving patient experiences was to apply management science principles such as Lean and Six Sigma to increase the efficiency of hospital operations. Though wait times decreased as a result, no attention was given to the "soft side" of customer service—the emotions and stresses customers face throughout their experience.

Through studying behavioral science, people have found ways to improve the patient experience on the soft side. For example, a study of behavioral science shows that the following improves the experience of waiting in lines (Chase and Dasu 2001):

- It is better to combine all of the waiting into the beginning of the experience.
- Customers do not notice how long they are waiting if they are distracted.
- Customers do not mind waiting long if they are able to track the progress of the item they are waiting on (e.g., the FedEx system that allows customers to track packages reduces anxiety and improves satisfaction).

By integrating these principles into the structure of queues, healthcare organizations can improve the patient experience without necessarily reducing the amount of time patients spend waiting.

Hospitals and health systems need to address not only the physical journey of the patient's experience but also the emotional one. Diagrams visualizing the emotional path of patients, which Dasu and Chase (2010) call Emotionprints, enable organizations to identify critical moments of truth that the organization needs to perform on. Emotionprints may also provide insight into the kind of emotional intelligence frontline staff need to exhibit at certain points in the service process (Dasu and Chase 2010). Meeting the emotional needs of customers appropriately and at the right time can help establish emotional bonds. These bonds build relationships with customers and may explain why Apple customers remain so loyal despite the availability of other products with comparable functionality and lower price (Noble and Kumar 2008).

Healthcare organizations can set the stage for certain emotional experiences before the patient even enters their facility. Companies use slogans to design an "emotional platform" from which customers are expected to base their experiences (Dasu and Chase 2010). For example, Nike's "Just Do It" campaign has little to do with athletic apparel and more to do with appealing to emotions such as the desire to be proactive and take charge of one's life. The recent "Believe in We" marketing campaign of OhioHealth, a health system based in Columbus, Ohio, aims in part to instill feelings of hope and togetherness in its patients. As a result, incoming patients are primed to look for these qualities throughout their experience.

WHAT THIS MEANS FOR HEALTHCARE ORGANIZATIONS

Delivering a great patient experience will be increasingly critical for hospitals to gain market share, increase profitability, and improve outcomes. As patients bear larger shares of healthcare costs (the popularity of high-deductible health plans more than tripled from 2007 to 2011, and nearly one-third of all plans come with a deductible of $1,000 or more [PwC 2012]), they will demand the value, convenience, and respect they receive from other industries. Research continues to confirm that patients choose hospitals on the basis of past experience, not clinical outcomes (Kaiser Family Foundation and AHRQ 2000; Grote, Newman, and Sutaria 2007; Abraham et al. 2011; Mintel 2011). Eighty percent of consumers now go online for health information, and 58 percent of those say their search affected their healthcare decision making

(Peterson 2011). Furthermore, half the U.S. population has delayed care or sought alternative medicine in 2011 because of the lack of perceived value in traditional healthcare (PwC 2012). Hospitals must embrace these trends as opportunities to learn more about their customers and shape services around the unique preferences of different customer segments.

A PROPOSED FRAMEWORK FOR OPTIMIZING PATIENT EXPERIENCE: THE THREE *PS*

Any healthcare organization wishing to improve its patients' experience should look beyond Hospital Consumer Assessment of Healthcare Providers and Systems (HCAHPS) and Press Ganey scores. Just as a thermometer measures temperature but does not reveal the disease that causes a fever, patient satisfaction scores record only symptoms, not the underlying causes. HCAHPS scores will soon be linked to 0.6 percent of reimbursement from Medicare, but the values that underlie delivering a great patient experience should be at the root of any healthcare organization regardless of compensation.

Patient experience is about managing both the emotional and physical roller coaster a patient experiences while undergoing a healthcare procedure and about maximizing the patient's social, mental, and physical health and wellness. To achieve this level of management, I propose a framework built around three Ps: personalize medicine, partner with patients, and empower employees.

P1: PERSONALIZE MEDICINE

Delivering personalized medicine requires keen understanding of the consumer and smart use of customer segmentation. Much like how Best Buy customizes its stores based on the customers who frequently shop in them, healthcare organizations need to tailor their delivery of services based on the demographics, technographics, and psychographics of their patients. Healthcare consumers are too often grouped into the same bucket—"patient"—without regard to their specific preferences or even biological composition. A closer examination of the patient may even reveal new strategies for improving patient care. For example, interventional video games have been shown to increase medication compliance rates and thus improve health outcomes among children (Kato et al. 2008).

While the scientific community is making great advances using the human genome to find the right drug for the right person, administrators need to personalize the delivery of the services to the patient. Creating patient segments is a start, but eventually healthcare organizations will be able to harness the power of "big data" and track every characteristic of every patient (Manyika et al. 2011). Already, healthcare organizations are introducing radio frequency identification technologies to customize the environment on the basis of patient preferences (Pfenninger et al. 2007).

P4 medicine, a concept developed by Leroy Hood, seeks to improve the quality of life through "predictive, preventive, personalized, and participatory medicine" (Nilsson 2006). The participatory element is especially important for healthcare organizations that want to improve their patients' experience. While the medical field is introducing incredible breakthroughs to improve health outcomes, no drug or service can do any good unless the patient is participating and engaged. Indeed, a 20 percent increase in compliance with medication plans has been shown to double survival chances in some patients (Richardson et al. 1990). Yet many discharge instructions are generic and contain information irrelevant to the patient, thus decreasing the probability of adherence (Lazerow et al. 2010). It therefore stands to reason that improving the patient experience through personalizing medicine also improves health outcomes.

P2: PARTNER WITH PATIENTS

Building partnerships with patients means engaging consumers through the continuum of care and is shown to lead to greater loyalty and better clinical outcomes (Grote, Newman, and Sutaria 2007; Fremont et al. 2001). This focus also allows an organization to be in tune with its patients' needs, paving the way for long-term success. Not only do patients who are involved in their own healthcare decisions experience better outcomes through adhering to plans for improved health, but they also are less likely to think negatively of a healthcare provider if adverse events do occur (Dasu and Chase 2010).

While organizations slowly adopt listening and connection-building strategies with their consumers, the rate at which the general public connects with each other increases exponentially due to advances in social technologies. Healthcare organizations should encourage patients who consider themselves partners with the provider to serve as advocates for the organization. Though data on clinical quality are readily available, patients still rely heavily on the opinions of family, friends, and acquaintances when making healthcare decisions. Indeed, 65 percent of patients in one study indicated that recommendations from family and friends were important in selecting a provider; informal sources were the second most popular source of information about a provider (Abraham et al. 2011). Therefore, improving the patient experience through the second P, partnering with patients, may be a crucial method of strengthening a healthcare organization's brand.

P3: EMPOWER EMPLOYEES

Addressing the first two Ps without the last one results in what business strategist and author Nilofer Merchant (2010) describes as an "air sandwich," meaning a strong strategy that is developed by the top level (healthcare administrators) and enforced at the bottom level (patients) without buy-in from the crucial middle mass (employees). Engaging employees may be the most important objective because the patient experience cannot improve unless both frontline and back-office employees buy into and consistently deliver on the promise. Studies show a correlation between patient satisfaction and employee engagement (e.g., Press Ganey 2010); this element cannot be overlooked by any organization wishing to become a top performer.

The objective goes beyond merely *engaging* employees, however; it requires *empowerment*. Physicians, nurses, house keepers, receptionists—all employees and staff—play an integral role in the experience a patient has within the continuum of care. Incidentally, they also happen to hold immense knowledge of the patients due to their repeated exposure to these consumers. Thus, staff members and associates are not only the most important individuals in delivering patient experience—*they are also the best suited to improve the patient experience*. No one knows the customer better than those who frequently interact with him or her, so it is important that employees at all levels of the organization feel empowered to do what they think is best for the patient. Additionally, engagement and autonomy are critical ingredients for a high-performing workforce (Pink 2009). Hence, the third P, empowering employees, is also about making sure the patient receives the best experience through every interaction with the organization.

CONCLUSION

It is easy to point to changing Medicare reimbursements or HCAHPS transparency and decide that an organization has a need to improve its patient satisfaction scores. Hospitals around the country are discovering methods such as post-discharge phone calls and nurse rounding to earn a boost in their ratings. However, addressing piecemeal symptoms such as these will at best achieve parity with competitors. The heart of the patient experience lies in the organization's ability to energize the unique employees, relationships, and services it offers, and to purposefully shape a positive experience that delivers on the brand's promise. By following the three Ps—personalizing medicine, partnering with patients, and empowering employees—healthcare organizations can use the resources they already have to simultaneously improve health outcomes; build brand power; and consistently serve the social, mental, and physical needs of the patients.

REFERENCES

Abraham, J., B. Sick, J. Anderson, A. Berg, C. Dehmer, and A. Tufano, 2011. "Selecting a Provider: What Factors Influence Patients' Decision Making?" *Journal of Healthcare Management* 56 (2): 95–114.

Aligning Forces for Quality 2010. *Good for Health, Good for Business*: *The Case for Measuring Patient Experience of Care, 1–7.* Princeton, NJ: Robert Wood Johnson Foundation. Accessed June 20, 2011. www.rwjf.org/files/research/71848.pdr.

Chase, R. B., and S. Dasu, 2001. "Want to Perfect Your Company's Service? Use Behavioral Science." *Harvard Business Review* 79(6): 78–84.

Cleveland Clinic, 2010. "2010 Patient Experience Summit: Session Summaries." Cleveland Clinic. Accessed March 23, 2012. www.clevelandclinic.org/ collective/2010summit/session_summaries.htm.

Dasu, S., and R. B. Chase, 2010. "Designing the Soft Side of Customer Service." *MIT Sloan Management Review* 52 (1): 33–39.

Freeman, K., and N. Toman, 2010. "Stop Trying to Delight Your Customers," *Harvard Business Review* 88 (7/8): 116–22.

Fremont, A. M., P. D. Cleary, J. L. Hargraves, R. M., Rowe, N. B. Jacobsen, and J. Z. Ayanian, 2001. "Patient-Centered Processes of Care and Long-Term Outcomes of Acute Myocardial Infarction." *Journal of General Internal Medicine* 16 (2): 800–808.

Grote, K. D., J. R. S. Newman, and S. S. Sutaria, 2007. "A Better Hospital Experience." *McKinsey Quarterly.* Published November 2007. www.mckinseyquarterly.com/ A_better_hospital_experience_2081.

Gulati, R. 2007. "Silo Busting: How to Execute on the Promise of Customer Focus." *Harvard Business Review* 85 (5): 98–108.

Hall, M. F. 2008. "Looking to Improve Financial Results? Start by listening to Patients." Healthcare Financial Management Association. Published October 1, www.hfma.org/Publications/hfm-Magazine/Archives/2008/October/ Looking-to-Improve-Financial-Results-Start-by-Listening-to-Patients/.

Kaiser Family Foundation and Agency for Healthcare Research and Quality (AHRQ). 2000. "National Survey on Americans as Health Care Consumers: An Update on the Role of Quality Information." Menlo Park, CA: Kaiser Family Foundation, Rockville, MD: Agency for Healthcare Research and Quality.

Kato, P., M., S. W. Cole, A. S. Bradlyn, and B. H. Pollock, 2008. "A Video Came Improves Behavioral Outcomes in Adolescents and Young Adults with Cancer: A Randomized Trial." *Pediatrics* 122 (2): e305–e317.

Lathrop, P. J. 1993. *Restructuring Health Care: The Patient Focused Paradigm.* San Francisco: Jossey-Bass.

Lazerow, R., C. Casey, K. Morgan, and C. Kerns. 2010. "Succeeding Under Bundled Payments: Reducing Readmissions and Protecting Hospital Profitability in an Era of Increasing Performance Risk." Washington, DC: The Advisory Board Company. Accessed June 20, 2011. www.advisory.com/~/media/Advisory-com/Research/HCAB/Research-Study/2010/Succeeding-Under-Bundled-Payments/Succeeding-Under-Bundled-Payments-HCAB.pdf.

Lecroy, N. 2010. "Anticipating the Changes in Medicare Reimbursement, the Beryl Institute's 2010 Conference Highlights Ideas on Improving Patient Experience," Bedford, TX: The Beryl Institute. Issued May 2010, www.theberylinstitute.org/resource/resmgr/press_releases/2010_tbi_post_conference.pdf.

Manyika, J., M. Chui, B. Brown, J. Bughin, R. Dobbs., C. Roxburgh, and A. H. Byers. 2011. *Big Data: The Next Frontier for Innovation, Competition, and Productivity.* McKinsey Global Institute. Published May 2011. www.mckinsey.com/Insights/MGI/Research/Technology_and_Innovation/Big_data_The_next_frontier_for_innovation.

Martin, R. L. 2011. "The Innovation Catalysts." *Harvard Business Review* 89 (6): 82–87.

Merchant, N. 2010. *The New How: Creating Business Solutions Through Collaborative Strategy.* Sabastopol, CA: O'Reilly Media.

Meyer, C., and A. Schwager, 2007. "Understanding Customer Experience." *Harvard Business Review* 85 (2): 116–26.

Mintel, 2011. "Attitudes Toward Hospitals—US." *Mintel Reports.* Published January 2011. http://store.mintel.com/attitudes-toward-hospitals-us-january-2011. html.

———. 2010. "Social Networking—US." *Mintel Reports.* Published February 2010. http://store.mintel.com/social-networking-us-february-2010.html.

Nilsson, E. 2006. "What Is P4 Medicine?" *P4 Medicine.* Accesssed March 23, 2012. http//blog.p4medicine.com/2006/07/what-is-p4-medicinc.html.

Noble, C., and M. Kumar. 2008. "Using Product Design Strategically to Create Deeper Consumer Connections." *Business Horizons* 51(5): 441–50.

Peterson, C. 2011. "The Voice of the Customer and Social Media Are Here to Stay." South Bend, IN: Press Ganey. Accessed June 20, 2011. http://www.pressganey. com/improvinghealthcare/improvinghcblog/blogPost/11-05-25/The_Voice_of_ thc_Customer_and_Social_Media_are_Here_to_Stay.aspx.

Pfenninger, D., T. Breen, S. Pollet, C. Schaal, M. Koppenheffer, and D. Hayes, 2007. "Designing the Consumer-Focused Facility: Aligning Facility Design with Marketing Preferences." Washington, DC: The Advisory Board Company. Accessed June 20, 2011. www.advisory.com/~/media/Advisory.com/Research/MPLC/ Research-Study/2008/Designing-the-Consumer-Focused-Facility/Designing-the-Consumer-Focused-Facility-MPLC.pdf.

Pink, D. H. 2009. *Drive: The Surprising Truth About What Motivates Us.* New York: Penguin.

Press Ganey, 2011. *2011 Pulse Report: Perspectives on American Health Care.* South Bend, IN: Press Ganey. Accessed June 20, 2011. www.pressganey.com/ Documents_secure/PulseReports/2011_Press_Caney_Pulse_Report.pdf?viewFile.

———. 2010. *2010 Pulse Report: Hospital.* South Bend, IN: Press Caney. Accessed June 20. 2011. www.pressganey.com/Documents_secure/Pulse%20Reports/ HOSPPulseReport_l2-28-2010.pdf?viewFile.

PwC. 2012. "Medical Cost Trend: Behind the Numbers 2013." New York: PwC Health
    Research Institute. Accessed June 12, 2012. http://pwchealth.com/cgi-local/
    hregister.cgi/reg/medical-cost-trend-behind-the-numbers-2013.pdf.

Reichheld, F. F. 2003. "The One Number You Need to Grow." *Harvard Business Review*
    81 (12): 46–54.

Richardson, J. L., D. R. Shelton, M. Krailo, and A. M. Levine, 1990 "The Effect of
    Compliance with Treatment on Survival Among Patients with Hematologic
    Malignancies." *Journal of Clinical Oncology* 8 (2): 356–64.

Rust, R. T., C. Moorman, and G. Bhalla, 2010. "Rethinking Marketing." *Harvard
    Business Review* 88 (1/2): 94–101.

INSPIRING INNOVATION: PATIENT REPORT OF HOURLY ROUNDING

USING PATIENT REPORT OF STAFF BEHAVIORS TO SUPPORT IMPROVEMENT EFFORTS

Behavior change can be difficult and feedback about the process is critical for success. When instituting any new process or improvement initiative, such as hourly rounding, the new behavior must either be fit into the existing repertoire or be conducted in place of a prior behavior or activity. With any newly instituted process, competing priorities will create a natural tendency to revert to what is comfortable and familiar, often at the expense of the new hourly rounding process. Implementing hourly rounding requires leadership commitment and a well-planned training process that includes information about the benefits of hourly rounding for patients and staff, the process that will be utilized, and the critical components or behaviors that are expected during the hourly round. Additionally, it reinforces the rounding process by demonstrating the impact and by tracking the frequency with which it is occurring.

For hourly rounding, checklists and logs can be used by staff both to prompt certain activities and to document the steps that have been taken (e.g., to document the round has taken place and to ensure specific issues are discussed with the patient). However, logs can lose their utility if they are completed retrospectively, not completed at all, or not tied to results. Alternatively, a peer or manager may directly observe the hourly rounding process and give either immediate or delayed feedback on what was observed. This offers the opportunity for rich feedback about the quality of the interaction and is especially useful when the rounding process is new, though can be time and staff intensive when used for long periods of time. Patients can offer valuable information regarding how care is being provided by incorporating survey questions into the ongoing measurement of patient experience. In this manner, patient report of staff behaviors can be directly tied to patient evaluations of the broader experience.

There are several important criteria to consider when selecting a behavior for patient feedback. The behavior must be something that occurs in front of the patient or has an outcome that is directly observable by the patient. The behavior should be something that the patient would typically notice if it occurs, rather than elements of the process that may not be immediately salient or understood by the patient. Finally, the benefit of using patients as sources of feedback should be balanced with the burden it places on them to report on specific aspects of their care. We should not ask patients to police every element of quality so should choose wisely among those being focused on for quality improvement initiatives for which the patient feedback will be actively used and shared.

Hourly rounding meets the above criteria. It occurs with the patient and is something the patient will likely notice and recall. Two critical insights can be gained when patients report on hourly rounding within the ongoing patient experience survey. First, the impact can be measured by comparing scores for patients who report experiencing hourly rounding vs. those who did not. Second, the frequency with which patients remember and recall hourly rounding occurring can be tracked as a measure of the adoption rate of the intended process. Organizations can track how often the behavior is occurring, whether adoption rate of the new process is improving, and which units are having greater success with the implementation.

Feedback to staff should focus first on the evidence supporting the impact of the behavior by showing the extent to which patient evaluations of care are higher when the hourly rounding occurs. This ties the process back to the shared purpose of the team, to make care better for their patients. It also allows for refinement of the rounding process if the desired benefit is not being reflected in patient evaluations. After the impact of the behavior is demonstrated, the trend for adopting the new process can be displayed as a reflection of current progress and encouragement to maintain and increase the use of hourly rounding.

NATIONAL RESULTS	
Study Population	• In 2013 there were 108 Press Ganey Inpatient clients asking the following question regarding hourly rounding: *Did a staff member visit you hourly during your stay? Yes/No* • Across those 108 client organizations, there were 120,164 patients who answered the question regarding hourly rounding.
Impact of Behavior	• Patients who reported experiencing hourly rounding during their stay reported higher evaluations of care in all areas across both Press Ganey measures and HCAHPS measures. All differences were statistically significant based upon independent *t*-tests (<.000). Results are displayed in the graphs below.

Difference in Press Ganey Section Scores: Hourly Rounding Yes vs. No

	Difference in Mean
OVERALL RATING	10.8
Admission Section	8.0
Room Section	9.9
Meals Section	8.7
Nurses Section	12.9
Tests and Treatments Section	9.4
Visitors and Family Section	9.4
Physician Section	10.0
Discharge Section	11.0
Personal Issues Section	13.0
Overall Assessment Section	13.6

- Differences in scores for individual Press Ganey measures ranged from +6.7 to +15.5. All differences were in favor of patients who stated that hourly occurred.
- The Nurses, Discharge, Personal Issues, and Overall Assessment section of the Press Ganey survey had individual items where the benefit of hourly rounding exceeded 10 points, most exceeding 12 points

Press Ganey Items Most Impacted by Hourly Rounding

	Difference in Mean
Nurses Section	12.9
Friendliness/courtesy of the nurses	9.6
Promptness in responding to the call button	15.1
Nurses' attitude toward your requests	12.3
Amount of attention paid to your special/ personal needs	14.6
How well the nurses kept you informed	14.8
Skill of the nurses	10.4
Discharge Section	11.0
Extent to which you felt ready to be discharged	8.4
Speed of discharge process	12.4
Instructions given about how to care for yourself at home	12.0
Personal Issues Section	13.0
Staff concern for your privacy	10.4
How well your pain was controlled	11.4
Degree to which staff addressed your emotional needs	13.8
Response to concerns/complaints made during your stay	15.5
Staff effort to include you in decisions re treatment	14.4
Overall Assessment Section	13.6
How well staff worked together to care for you	12.7
Likelihood of your recommending this hospital to others	14.4
Overall rating of care given at hospital	13.3

- The Press Ganey items that hourly rounding had the largest impact on was: *Response to concerns and complaints made during your stay* (+15.5) and *Promptness in responding to the call button* (+15.1).
- Based on the findings above, the practice of hourly rounding appears to influence the way a patient perceives nursing care overall, as well as many of the more intangible attributes of care. Notably, patients perceive *Response to concerns and complaints* to be higher when they have been visited on an hourly basis. This may reflect both the opportunity to be asked about any concerns they have, the process of being listened to, and the ability for a nurse or staff member to address the patient concerns in the moment and provide resolution. Additionally, the practice of hourly rounding results in dramatically higher scores for promptness in response to the call button. The rounding process is expected to dramatically reduce the frequency with which patients need to use the call button, so nursing staff may be able to respond more quickly to the patients when they do use the call system.

HCAHPS Items Most Impacted by Hourly Rounding

	Difference in Top Box
RN Communication	
Nurse courtesy	21.0%
Nurse listen	27.0%
Nurse explain	24.5%
Staff Responsiveness	
Response to call button	27.5%
Assistance with toileting	25.5%
Dr Communication	
Doctor courtesy	13.3%
Doctor listen	17.5%
Doctor explain	17.8%
Pain Control	
Pain controlled	22.5%
Staff do everything to help pain	24.9%
Info re New Meds	
Told what new meds were for	22.9%
Described new meds side effects	29.2%
Info re Discharge	
Asked re help needed post discharge	16.1%
Info in writing re symptoms to look for	10.4%
Transition to Home	
Staff took preferences into account	24.1%
Understand manage health	23.8%
Understand purpose of meds	20.6%
Global	
Rate hospital 0-10	29.1%
Likelihood of recommending hospital	26.7%

	• Patients who experience hourly rounding are more likely to report top box ratings across all HCAHPS measures. • The impact of hourly rounding is particularly noticeable for the global items as well as the areas of nurse communication and responsiveness.

Innovation Stories are intended to highlight case studies and examples of organizations successfully applying a quality improvement strategy to innovate and improve. This Innovation Story demonstrates the effectiveness of using patient report of staff behaviors to support improvement initiatives.

REFLECTIONS ON THE READING SELECTIONS

We offer the following editorial commentary on the reading selections.

1. In the article by Needham (2012) on p. 202, he uses the term "consumers' lifetime value." This term encompasses the total economic value of a particular customer throughout their lifetime. In marketing, it is important to not just focus on one-time service encounters because in reality, patients and/or their families will most likely need healthcare services throughout their lives. As healthcare providers, it is important to establish a long-term relationship with our patients and their family members to increase customer loyalty and overall satisfaction with the services provided.

2. Typically in marketing, we use the marketing mix, which consists of the 4Ps (Product, Price, Place, Promotion). However, in Needham's article (2012), the author identifies three specific Ps. We want to make sure that you do not confuse the 4Ps in the marketing mix with the 3Ps of the proposed framework to improve the patient experience.

3. The 2014 article by the Institute for Innovation is only one of many useful articles that provide concrete examples on how to improve the patient experience. We encourage you to explore the many resource articles provided by www.TheInstituteForInnovation.org.

APPLICATION AND SYNTHESIS

"They may forget your name, but they will never forget how you made them feel." —*Maya Angelou* (Sweeney, 2014)

QUESTIONS FOR DISCUSSION

1. What industry do you believe the healthcare industry can use as a model to create a better patient experience?

2. What industries do you believe are the most consumer-centric and provide the best experience and why?

3. What do you believe are the key elements in the patient experience and why?

4. How can HCAHPS provide insight into improving the patient experience?

5. When could a healthcare organization have high HCAHPS scores and a poor patient experience?

6. Place yourself in the patient experience—what are the key components that would be important to you?

SUMMARY OF MAIN POINTS

After reading this chapter, you should be able to:

√ Discuss the terms patient-centered care, patient satisfaction, and patient experience (p. 197-199)
√ Apply best practices from other industries to a healthcare organization (p. 200)
√ Examine HCAHPS scores to identify areas where staff impact the patient experience (p. 214-215)

COMPREHENSION ASSESSMENT

1. What is the difference between patient satisfaction and the patient experience?

2. What are some examples of businesses that have focused on establishing strong customer relationships?

3. What are the 3Ps for optimizing the patient experience?

4. In the study by Press Ganey in 2013, what was the impact of hourly rounding? What areas were impacted the most by hourly rounding?

CONCLUSION

In this chapter, we discussed patient-centered care, patient satisfaction, and the patient experience. We hope that you will begin to approach healthcare services from a different perspective that is focused on creating a memorable experience for patients and their family members.

In the final chapter, we will discuss the issue of ethics in marketing and, in particular, in the healthcare industry.

REFERENCES

Sweeney, A. (2014). *37 inspiring quotes to motivate healthcare employees*. Retrieved from http://www.hospitalportal.net/blog/bid/391882/37-inspiring-quotes-to-motivate-healthcare-employees.

Lee Scher, D. (2012). *How patient-centric care differs from patient-centered care*. Retrieved from https://davidleescher.com/2012/03/03/how-patient-centric-care-differs-from-patient-centered-care-2/.

IMAGE CREDITS

- Fig. 7.0: Copyright © Depositphotos/Siempreverde.
- Fig. 7.2: Copyright © Depositphotos/andrewgenn.
- Fig. 7.3: Copyright © Depositphotos/ursem.cs.au.dk.
- Fig. 7.4: Copyright © Depositphotos/ncousla.

8

CHAPTER

ETHICS AND HEALTHCARE MARKETING

LEARNING OBJECTIVES

In this chapter, you will learn about the following:

- Ethical conflicts that may occur in a healthcare setting
- Impact of HIPAA on medical marketing
- Organizational costs of ethical conflicts

INTRODUCTION

A question that is often asked by healthcare professionals is, "Is marketing ethical?" The issue of ethics is quite complex, particularly in healthcare, where providers are guided by codes of medical ethics. Healthcare organizations should always be guided by ethical principles, which should also include their marketing initiatives because they are held to a higher standard than other types of organizations.

NOTES FROM PRACTICE

Figure 8.1 Beth Israel Logo

ETHICS BRIEF—BETH ISRAEL DEACONESS MEDICAL CENTER

Marianna V. Mapes, 2016–2017 Ethics Programs Intern

Lachlan Forrow, MD, Director of Ethics Programs

Wendy McHugh, RN, MS, Associate Director of Ethics Programs

Steve O'Neill, LICSW, BCD, JD, Associate Director of Ethics Programs and Social Work Manager

MISSION STATEMENT—ETHICS PROGRAMS AT BETH ISRAEL DEACONESS MEDICAL CENTER

To promote a culture in which all BIDMC staff appreciate the importance of the ethical aspects of their work (their decisions, actions, character, and morale), and have the support they need to do that work in accordance with BIDMC's and their own highest moral standards.

Ethics Programs at Beth Israel Deaconess Medical Center comprise the Ethics Support Service, the Ethics Liaison Program, and the Ethics Advisory Committee. These core facets of Ethics Programs work synergistically to support a flourishing moral community at BIDMC. The overarching theme of Ethics Programs—"Ethics Is Everyone"—reflects our deep commitment to ensuring that our culture of ethics embraces every member of the BIDMC community.

ETHICS SUPPORT SERVICE (ESS)

One of the functions of the ESS is to provide consultation, supporting staff, patients, and their families in ensuring that care reflects the highest moral standards of BIDMC. The ESS consists of three staff members who provide 10–20 inpatient and outpatient consults per month for any staff member, patient, or family member who wishes to discuss an ethical issue. The ethics consultant facilitates discussion with the stakeholders at the unit level. Throughout the process, the attending physician remains in charge of the patient's care. In striving to support staff in their commitment to providing the best care, the ESS may meet with patients and family members to assist in navigating areas where there is uncertainty or conflict and to support a process of shared decision-making. Concurrently with these consults, the ESS provides 20 unit-based ethics rounds each month, which adopt a preventive ethics approach. These unit-based rounds allow discussion of ethical conflicts and questions in an informal setting, thereby supporting staff in developing their ethical thinking and cultivating a deep moral awareness of their work at the Medical Center.

In addition, the ESS staff provides a great deal of formal education through grand rounds, plenary talks, workshops, courses, and training sessions. The ESS also assists the Medical Center, its affiliates, and state and federal agencies in the development and oversight of issues related to organizational ethics, including policy guidelines.

ETHICS LIAISONS PROGRAM

Our Ethics Liaisons comprise a critical infrastructure of staff members that extends the reach of Ethics Programs at BIDMC and reinforces our institutional mission. The designation of an Ethics Liaison to represent each area of hospital activity, whether clinical or administrative, establishes a bidirectional conduit that (a) makes ethics resources accessible to each department/division and (b) allows both individual liaisons and Ethics Programs at large to remain apprised of and responsive to matters of ethical import across the Medical Center.

The program offers a forum for reflection and discussion that is both centralized and inclusive. Liaisons meet monthly to discuss recent redacted ethics cases and consider readings on a variety of salient topics in ethics. These meetings foster robust staff engagement and education and position Ethics Liaisons to act as ethics champions in their work. Each year, liaisons are asked to design and complete an ethics-related project in their respective departments, providing an opportunity to further integrate BIDMC's core values into their work, address areas of departmental need and/or interest, and raise awareness among their colleagues of the ethics resources at the Medical Center.

ETHICS ADVISORY COMMITTEE (EAC)

As its name suggests, the EAC functions in a strictly advisory capacity. The EAC reports annually to the Medical Executive Committee and convenes monthly to review the activities of the Ethics Support Service, discuss the development and utilization of ethics resources at the Medical Center, and, where relevant, participate in policy formation. The EAC's broad-based membership includes clinicians, non-clinical staff, and community representatives, all of whom contribute rich perspectives to the ongoing development of ethics resources at BIDMC.

Most recently, Ethics Programs have been repositioned within the Department of Health Care Quality. This new organizational structure suits the wide-reaching scope of Ethics Programs' activities and allows for further support of institutional initiatives, as well as broader priorities around improving the quality of patient care and advancing a culture of respect and dignity at the Medical Center.

ETHICAL DECISIONS—CASE STUDY

WORKPLACE ETHICAL CONFLICT

Brandy J. Meadows, MBA

In late May 2016, a 45-year-old female, Jane*, scheduled an elective hernia repair surgery at Memorial Hospital*. The hernia area was not infected and did not require repair unless desired by the patient. Jane is 5 feet tall and weighs 192 pounds. Though overweight, Jane was otherwise a healthy female patient.

Jane came in to have blood drawn for routine laboratory tests two days prior to surgery. For unknown reasons, her laboratory test results were not evaluated until Jane came in for surgery. At that time, the anesthesiologist saw Jane had low potassium levels. Typically, this is an easy correction to make in the body's physiology. At this point, the patient was at the hospital and awaiting surgery. The surgery was scheduled as the last sur-

"Workplace conflict?"

Figure 8.2 Workplace Conflicts Must Be Addressed

gery of the day. An hour before surgery, the anesthesiologist called the hospital pharmacist to request the amount of potassium needed to bring Jane up to the correct levels before she went into surgery. When the pharmacist reviewed the request, she saw the anesthesiologist wanted to administer a large amount of potassium in a short period of time. Specifically, the anesthesiologist was requesting 60 mEq to be administered in one hour.

To ensure safe administration of potassium replacement solutions, the hospital created a policy. The policy is as follows:

	MAX CONCENTRATION	MAX DISPENSE QUANTITY	MAX RATE
Med/Surg Beds	**Peripheral/Central Line:** 10 mEq/100mL	**Continuous Infusion:** 40 mEq/liter	10 mEq/hr
Monitored Tele Beds and Emergency Rooms	Same as Med/Surg Beds	Same as Med/Surg Beds	20 mEq/hr
ICU Beds	**Peripheral Line:** 10 mEq/100mL **Central or Larger Vein:** 20 mEq/100mL	**Continuous Infusion:** 40 mEq/liter	20 mEq/hr

- Potassium chloride should always be given through a properly functioning IV pump as a slow infusion.
- The maximum suggested bolus dose of potassium is 40 mEq at one time.
- When the estimated rates of potassium infusion from ALL sources (i.e., PN, maintenance IVF, bolus IV) exceeds **40 mEq/hour** in patients in **monitored beds**, the authorizing physician should be notified.
- When the estimated rates of potassium infusion from ALL sources (i.e., PN, maintenance IVF, bolus IV) exceeds **20 mEq/hour** in patients in **unmonitored beds**, the authorizing physician should be notified.

The pharmacist denied the request of the anesthesiologist, pointing out the hospital policy for potassium administration. If given too fast, potassium can greatly affect the heart rate and rhythm. The anesthesiologist stated he had successfully administered 60 mEq in an hour before in other surgical cases. Since the surgery was scheduled late in the day, a slower potassium administration would mean the surgery would need to be rescheduled or the surgeon would have to wait several hours to perform the surgery that day. The anesthesiologist did not want to postpone an elective surgery or keep the surgeon waiting.

The pharmacist reached out to a hospital cardiologist to talk about the administration of a high level of potassium in a short amount of time. The cardiologist stated it could be done, but it would only be during a critical time, usually during a heart surgery when the heart was already accessible. He stated he would never risk giving 60 mEq in an hour for an elective surgery that was unrelated to the heart. This administration would cause a significant risk to the patient. Also, the pharmacist believed the patient's blood work needed more review to determine why the potassium levels were low.

The pharmacist denied the request to forgo hospital policy in the administration of potassium at a dose of 60 mEq/hour. The surgery was postponed, and oral potassium was prescribed to the patient.

Unfortunately, Jane was unhappy with the delayed surgery. The postponement caused a variety of inconveniences for her. Jane rescheduled surgery for the next week. At the time, her potassium levels, as well as other blood work, were at satisfactory levels. The elective hernia repair surgery was successful.

1. How is this case a marketing issue?

2. How does rescheduling surgery when a patient has already checked in impact patient satisfaction?

3. Does anything change in the decision-making because this surgery was a low-risk elective surgery?

4. When should a hospital policy be questioned and possibly overridden by anesthesiologists, pharmacists, physicians, and other staff?

"And now round two of 'Justify It'. We'll start with you."

Figure 8.3 Fast Ethics Check—What Would Your Mother Say?

5. What could have been done to prevent this from happening?

*Jane and Memorial Hospital are fictitious names that represent a real person and a real hospital.

MEDICAL ETHICS

CODE OF MEDICAL ETHICS

Since 1847, the AMA *Code of Medical Ethics* (www.ama-assn.org) has outlined the values to which physicians commit themselves. It offers guidance to physicians in meeting the ethical challenges that occur when practicing medicine. A revised edition was adopted in June 2016. The code is periodically reviewed and updated to ensure that it remains a relevant resource.

AMERICAN MEDICAL ASSOCIATION PRINCIPLES OF MEDICAL ETHICS

The American Medical Association's Code of Medical Ethics provides the following list of ethical principles:

1. A physician shall be dedicated to providing competent medical care, with compassion and respect for human dignity and rights.

2. A physician shall uphold the standards of professionalism, be honest in all professional interactions, and strive to report physicians deficient in character or competence, or engaging in fraud or deception, to appropriate entities.

3. A physician shall respect the law and also recognize a responsibility to seek changes in those requirements which are contrary to the best interests of the patient.

4. A physician shall respect the rights of patients, colleagues, and other health professionals, and shall safeguard patient confidences and privacy within the constraints of the law.

5. A physician shall continue to study, apply, and advance scientific knowledge, maintain a commitment to medical education, make relevant information available to patients, colleagues, and the public, obtain consultation, and use the talents of other health professionals when indicated.

6. A physician shall, in the provision of appropriate patient care, except in emergencies, be free to choose whom to serve, with whom to associate, and the environment in which to provide medical care.

7. A physician shall recognize a responsibility to participate in activities contributing to the improvement of the community and the betterment of public health.

8. A physician shall, while caring for a patient, regard responsibility to the patient as paramount.

9. A physician shall support access to medical care for all people.

The University of Ottawa developed the Four Traditional Pillars of Medical Ethics (www.med.uottawa.ca), which provide a good explanation of ethical reasoning and arguments with healthcare situations. These include:

1. "Respect for *autonomy* of the patient. Autonomy refers to the capacity to think, decide, and act on one's own free initiative. Physicians and family members therefore should help the patient come to their own decision by providing full information; they should also uphold a competent, adult patient's decision, even if it appears medically wrong.

2. *Beneficence*: promoting what is best for the patient. The general moral principle of doing good to others is focused by the lens of being in a professional caring relationship. The definition of 'what is best' may derive from the health professional's judgment or the patient's wishes (see Autonomy); these are generally in agreement, but may diverge. Beneficence implies consideration of the patient's pain; their physical and mental suffering; the risk of disability and death; and their quality of life. At times, beneficence can imply not intervening, if the benefit of therapy would be minimal.

3. *Non-maleficence*: do no harm. In most cases of treating sick patients this adds little to the beneficence principle. But most treatments involve some degree of risk or have side-effects, so this principle reminds us to ponder the possibility of doing harm, especially when you cannot cure. May there be harmful consequences of labeling this patient as having bipolar disorder? In dealing with healthy people (e.g., preventive care, immunizations), do the benefits outweigh the potential harms? Remember that medicine has a long history of doing harm. In the 18th and early 19th century, surgery was highly lethal and giving birth in [a] hospital led to higher maternal mortality than home births.

4. *Justice*. Resources are limited; you cannot cure everybody and so priorities must be set (hence the notion of triage). In allocating care, the Justice principle holds that patients in similar situations should have access to the same care, and that in allocating resources to one group we should assess the impact of this choice on others. In effect, is what the patient is asking for fair? Will it lead to a burden to others (such as the family caregivers)? While your primary duty is to your patient, others will be affected by your decisions and there may be a tension between beneficence, autonomy, and justice."

MEDICAL MARKETING

There are some guiding marketing principles with regard to communications with consumers. Just as with the AMA Code of Ethics, organizations should provide a *Code of Ethics* that states the professional responsibility of people within the organization. It may also discuss difficult decisions that will occur frequently and provide direction on what is considered ethical or correct with regard to the organization's circumstances.

Electronic Marketing is the use of electronic media and applications to communicate with potential customers. Electronic marketing is analogous to *digital marketing*, which is the use of electronic media to promote products or brands, allowing real-time analysis of results.

Opt In is a term that is used in respect to email or other direct electronic communications. When someone opts in, they agree to receive some form of electronic communication; it is also referred to as permission-based marketing.

*Opt Out i*s when someone takes action to not receive forms of direct electronic communication. Examples would be someone clicking links to opt out of email communications. In this form of permission, someone must actively choose not to receive the communication.

**"I suppose I'll be the one
to mention the elephant in the room."**

Figure 8.4 Code of Ethics Facilitate Open
Discussion of Conflicts

READING SELECTIONS

READING 8.1

MARKETING TO PATIENTS: A LEGAL AND ETHICAL PERSPECTIVE

BY DEBORAH M. GRAY (DEBORAH.GRAY@CMICH.EDU)
AND LINDA CHRISTIANSEN (LCHRISTI@IU.EDU)

INTRODUCTION

The healthcare industry appears to be avoiding use of email and Web marketing as a result of concerns regarding HIPAA restrictions and warnings from insurers not to engage in electronic communication with consumers (Landro, 2002). In this paper we address the use of electronic marketing strategies (email marketing, online scheduling, etc.) in the healthcare field within the confines of the HIPAA law and industry-recommended ethical guidelines. Offering these customer-oriented services can be a strategic use of the Internet for marketing to current patients, attracting new patients, and reducing costs. Web and email marketing are ripe marketing options for medical practices because consumers are increasingly using the Internet as a means of searching for information about their health concerns (HarrisInteractive, 2007). Today's patients are very interested in being able to contact their physician by email to schedule appointments and/or ask questions (HarrisInteractive, 2007). However, these services must be offered within the realm of legal rules (HIPPA) and ethical guidelines set forth by industry codes of ethics.

Research clearly shows that Americans are avid users of the Internet for healthcare matters. According to industry reports from 2004, 78% of American consumers have Internet access and 97% have email access at home, work, or via a friend (HarrisInteractive, 2004). In that study, nearly 74% of U.S. adults reported that they use the Internet to search for medical information (HarrisInteractive, 2004); and in 2007, another 58% felt so empowered by the available information that they brought those concerns to their physician (HarrisInteractive, 2007). The number of people who have searched for medical information online has seen a 37% increase in the two year period from 2005 to 2007 (160 million in 2007 from 117 million in 2005) (HarrisInteractive, 2007). HarrisInteractive has coined the term "cyberchondriacs" to describe the 84% of adults who go online to search for medical information (HarrisInteractive, 2007). As long ago as 2000, 54% of consumers felt strongly enough about email communications to schedule appointments, renew prescriptions, or check lab results that they would be willing to switch doctors to one who offers such (Coile, 2000). Taken together, most people are searching for health-related information online, and they are discussing that information with their doctors. More than half want to use email in some capacity to communicate with their doctor. What does this mean to doctors, healthcare professionals, and medical practices?

> "The huge and growing numbers of 'cyberchondriacs' who use the Internet to look for health information and to help them have better conversations with their doctors has surely had a big impact on the knowledge of patients, the questions they ask their doctors, and is therefore changing the doctor-patient relationship and the practice of medicine. There is every reason to believe the impact of the Internet on medical practice will continue to grow." (HarrisInteractive, 2007)

It is clear that if medical practices are going to reach consumers with information about their services or engage in customer retention activities, they cannot ignore email and Web marketing strategies. However, they also cannot ignore the law or ethical standards set forth by the marketing industry. The constraint then for taking advantage of online marketing strategies in the medical field is two-pronged—both legal and ethical. From a legal perspective, many people have the misconception that HIPAA prohibits any release or use of medical information for most reasons. Bizarre interpretations of the law range from the cancellation of birthday parties for nursing home residents for fear of revealing a resident's date of birth to assigning nonsense code names in lieu of patient names for summoning people from doctor's waiting rooms. Some medical personnel have taken to blaming HIPAA when refusing to reveal medical information, whether by innocence or intentionally (Gross, 2007). Once healthcare organizations overcome the "fear" of HIPAA, they must then take into consideration the ethical guidelines from organizations like The American Marketing Association and The Direct Marketing Association.

This paper addresses the legal and ethical concerns for marketing methods which use the Internet or other forms of electronic media to market to current patients using their medical records.

HEALTH INSURANCE PORTABILITY AND ACCOUNTABILITY ACT OF 1996 (HIPAA)

HIPAA was enacted in 1996 because, among other reasons, Congress wanted to reduce the cost of administrative operations in the healthcare industry. Electronic transfer of healthcare information was becoming more prominent and was thought to be part of the solution. The act sought to simplify the exchange of electronic information, while also guarding against fraud and unauthorized access and disclosure to health information. As with many substantial passages of laws, Congress delegated the duty to issue regulations to a federal agency, the Department of Health and Human Services (HHS), regarding the how, when, and to what extent private health information can be disclosed (HIPAA sections 261–264).

The major goal of the Privacy Rule is to protect patients' health information while striking a balance to allow for sufficient flow of medical information to provide high quality healthcare and to protect the public's health and well-being (Office of Civil Rights, Summary of the HIPAA Privacy Rule 4).

The Privacy Rule covers all "protected health information" (PHI), which includes all individually identifiable health information that is held or transmitted by the covered entity or its business associate.

Individually identifiable health information is information that is a subset of health information, including demographic information collected from an individual, and

1. Is created or received by a healthcare provider, health plan, employer, or healthcare clearinghouse; and

2. Relates to the past, present, or future physical or mental health or condition of an individual; the provision of healthcare to an individual; or the past, present, or future payment for the provision of healthcare to an individual; and

   i. That identifies the individual; or

ii. With respect to which there is a reasonable basis to believe the information can be used to identify the individual (45 CFR 160.103).

For purposes of HIPAA, "covered entities" include (1) a health plan; (2) a healthcare clearinghouse; or (3) a healthcare provider who transmits any health information in electronic form in connection with a transaction covered by this subchapter. A "healthcare provider" is defined as "a provider of services, a provider of medical or health services, and any other person or organization who furnishes, bills, or is paid for healthcare in the normal course of business" (45 CFR 160.103,104).

MARKETING ETHICS

Medical professionals need to study and reflect beyond the legal restrictions imposed by HIPAA. In regards to marketing, medical professionals should employ a three-tiered approach in evaluating the appropriateness of behavior. First, the intent of law is generally thought to be the minimum acceptable behavior, rather than the ideal. Second, ethical standards demand more in that they are based on what is right, rather than the minimum that will be enforced by the legal system. Finally, marketing activities by definition carry the even greater burden of attracting and appealing to the target audience.

Though the American Medical Association has an extensive code of ethics, it does not specifically address the issue of marketing to patients—the focus is on dedication to the best interest of the patient's health which includes following the law (American Medical Association, 2008). Of course this is no surprise since the American Medical Association is a medical association. The American Marketing Association (AMA) serves all organizations who engage in any form of marketing, including Internet marketing. The Direct Marketing Association (DMA) serves organizations that market directly to the consumer; therefore the DMA has more specific and rigorous ethical guidelines for online marketing. The AMA Code of Ethics requires that members conform to three ethical norms of conduct and 6 ethical values (AMA Code of Ethics, 2008).

- "Marketers must do no harm."
- "Marketers must foster truth and trust in the marketing system."
- "Marketers must embrace, communicate, and practice the fundamental ethical values that will improve consumer confidence in the integrity of the marketing exchange system. These basic values are intentionally aspirational and include honesty, responsibility, fairness, respect, openness, and citizenship." Within its

Code of Ethics, the AMA defers to sub-disciplines to create and define industry-specific codes of ethics.

The DMA is one of these industry sub-disciplines. The DMA has 54 articles within its 31-page "Guidelines for Ethical Business Practice," including articles 38–43 which address online marketing (DMA's Guidelines for Ethical Business Practice, 2008). Table 8.1 summarizes the contents of articles 38–43. The DMA ethical guidelines focus primarily on providing notice and consent to consumers. Note however, that the DMA does not discourage marketers from using cookies (small pieces of software placed on your computer that identify you—without cookies your login information is not saved on a Web site, for example). Marketers who follow The DMA guidelines

TABLE 8.1 SUMMARY OF THE DMA GUIDELINES FOR ETHICAL BUSINESS PRACTICE

ARTICLE	SUMMARY OF ETHICAL GUIDELINES
38: Online Marketing	Marketers must provide notice, honor choice, provide access, provide data security, abide by laws and ethical guidelines that apply to marketing to children under the age of 13, and demonstrate accountability.
39: Commercial Solicitations Online	Marketers may send commercial email solicitations if they are sent to the marketers' own customers, or the customer has agreed to receive solicitations, or the customer did not "opt out" when given the choice to do so. Within each email solicitation, marketers must provide customers with a notice and an Internet-based way to refuse future solicitations or request that the marketer not rent, sell, or exchange their email information for online solicitation purposes.
40: E-Mail Authentication	Marketers that use email for communication and transaction purposes should adopt and use protocols that readily identify who they are.
41: Use of Software...	Marketers should not deceptively install or use software that interferes with the consumer's computer including software that produces endless loop pop ups, viruses, or spam. If the marketer does install software on the consumer's computer the marketer must provide notice and a method for uninstalling the software. This article does not govern the use of cookies. Cookies are governed by article 38.
42: Online Referral Marketing	Online referral marketing includes encouraging the consumer to forward information to another consumer *or* to provide the marketer with personally identifiable information about another person (e.g., a friend's email address). The guidelines in this article only apply to the second item aforementioned and require that if the marketer is going to engage in using email addresses provided by another consumer, the marketer must tell the referring user what the information will be used for. They must also disclose if the referring user's own information will also be used and disclose to the referred individual that their information was obtained by a referral, and provide a way for all individuals to be removed from future contact.

43: Email Appending to Consumer Records	Email appending is the act of connecting an individual's email address to another record (e.g., name, physical address, etc.) via a third party database. Marketers should append consumer records only when the consumer gives permission to do so, *or* when there is an established relationship with the consumer, *or* the consumer did not "opt out" via the third party database collector, and efforts are made to verify the accuracy of the append. All messages to an e-mail appended address should disclose notice and choice to continue to communicate via email.

will mention the use of cookies somewhere in their privacy or terms of use statement. We also note that the DMA does not actively encourage "permission-based" marketing within their ethical guidelines (nor do they discourage it).

MARKETING CONSIDERATIONS IN HEALTHCARE INDUSTRIES

However, if healthcare organizations choose to offer these services, they should also follow the DMA Ethical Guidelines requiring that all emails include a notice and an Internet-based method for "opting out" of future email solicitations. Because of the sensitivity of health-related information, we believe healthcare organizations should take *extra* precaution when using online strategies by using only an "opt in" approach, otherwise known as permission-based marketing. While it is within the DMA guidelines to contact consumers until or if they "opt out," consumers are understandably sensitive when it comes to their healthcare-related information. It is therefore not only ethical, *but judicious*, to adopt an "opt in" strategy for medically-related online marketing strategies.

The medical industry has missed an opportunity to market to patients and to offer patients value by offering services via email because of fear of violating HIPPA regulations. This need not be the case. From a legal and ethical perspective, as long as medical practices do not sell or rent a patient's personal information to a third party, they can use email to market to new and existing services to patients without breaking the law or ethical guidelines set forth by the DMA. Moreover, they can offer value-added services which will likely result in gaining new patients. The three tiered approach is not only legal and ethical, but judicious: follow the HIPPA Law, operate within the guidelines of industry ethical standards, and carry a greater burden of asking "Will I offend my patient/customer," "What concerns might my patient/customer have with this strategy?"

REFERENCES

42 USC 1320d-6(a)(3), (HIPAA Sec. 1177)

45 CFR 160.103 (2002).

45 CFR 160.103,104 (2003).

45 CFR 164.501(1), Federal Register, Vol. 67, No. 157, August 14, 2002, pp.
   53183–4, http://www.hhs.gov/ocr/hipaa/privrulepd.pdf (last accessed
   August 23, 2008).

45 CFR Subtitle A, Part 164.104(a)(3), http://www.access.gpo.gov/nara/cfr/waisidx
   06/45cfr164 06.html. (last accessed August 23, 2008).

American Marketing Association Statement of Ethics (2008), http://www.
   marketingpower.com/AboutAMA/Pages/Statement%20of%20Ethics.a spx,
   (last accessed August 23, 2008).

American Medical Association Principles of Ethics (2008). http://www.ama-assn.
   org/ama/pub/category/2512.html (last accessed August 23, 2008).

Coile, Russell C. Jr (2000). E-health: Reinventing healthcare in the information age.
   Journal of Healthcare Management, 45(3), 206–10.

Direct Marketing Association's Guidelines for Ethical Business Practice (2008)
   http://www.dmaresponsibility.org/Guidelines/, (last accessed August 23, 2008).

Gross, Jane, "Keeping Patients' Details Private, Even From Kin," The New York Times,
   July 3, 2007, http://www.nytimes.com/2007/07/03/health/policy/03hipaa.
   html? r=1&oref=slogin (last accessed August 23, 2008).

HarrisInteractive (2007). "Harris Poll Shows Number of 'Cyberchondriacs'—Adults
   Who Have Ever Gone Online for Health Information—Increases to an Estimated
   160 Million Nationwide," *The Harris Poll #76*, July 31.

HarrisInteractive (2004). "No Significant Change in the Number of
   'Cyberchondriacs'—Those Who go Online for Medical Information, http://www.

harrisi.org/news/newsletters/healthnews/HI HealthCareNews2004Vol 4 Iss00
7.pdf. (last accessed January 24, 2007), 4 (7).

Health Information Privacy and Civil Rights Questions & Answers, Question 281,
http://www.hhs.gov/hipaafag/use/281.html (last accessed August 23, 2008).

HIPAA sections 261–264, http://aspe.hhs.gov/admnsimp/pl104191.htm (last
accessed August 23, 2008).

Landro, Laura (2002) "New Guidelines to Make Doctor-Patient E-Mails Profitable,
Less Risky" *Wall Street Journal (Eastern Edition)*, New York, N.Y.: Jan 25
pg A. 13.

Office for Civil Rights, U.S. Dept. of Health & Human Services, Summary of the
HIPAA Privacy Rule 4, p. 1, last revised 05/2003, http://www.hhs.gov/ocr/
privacysummary.pdf, (last accessed August 23, 2008).

State Health Privacy Laws (2nd edition, 2002), www.healthprivacy.org at http://
www.healthprivacy.org/info-url nocat2304/info-url nocat.htm, (last accessed
August 23, 2008).

READING 8.2

THE ORGANIZATIONAL COSTS OF ETHICAL CONFLICTS

BY WILLIAM A. NELSON, WILLIAM B. WEEKS, AND JUSTIN M. CAMPFIELD

EXECUTIVE SUMMARY

Ethical conflicts are a common phenomenon in today's healthcare settings. As healthcare executives focus on balancing quality care and cost containment, recognizing the
costs associated with ethical conflicts is only logical. In this article, we present five
case vignettes to identify several general cost categories related to ethical conflicts,
including operational costs, legal costs, and marketing and public relations costs. In

each of these cost categories, the associated direct, indirect, and long-term costs of the ethical conflict are explored as well.

Our analysis suggests that organizations have, in addition to philosophical reasons, financial incentives to focus on decreasing the occurrence of ethical conflicts. The cost categories affected by ethical conflicts are not insignificant. Such conflicts can affect staff morale and lower the organization's overall culture and profit margin. Therefore, organizations should develop mechanisms and strategies for decreasing and possibly preventing ethical conflicts.

The strategies suggested in this article seek to shift the organization's focus when dealing with conflicts, from just reacting to moving upstream—that is, understanding the root causes of ethical conflicts and employing approaches designed to reduce their occurrence and associated costs. Such an effort has the potential to enhance the organization's overall culture and ultimately lead to organizational success.

For more information on the concepts in this article, please contact Dr. Nelson at william.a.nelson@dartmouth.edu. The views expressed in this article do not necessarily represent the views of the U.S. Department of Veterans Affairs (VA) or of the U.S. government. Dr. Nelson acknowledges that some thoughts in this manuscript grew from discussions with past colleagues and summer interns at the VA's National Center for Ethics in Health Care.

Ethical conflicts are a common occurrence in healthcare facilities. Managing and responding to the ethical conflict can be challenging because inherent in all ethical conflicts is uncertainty or the question of what appropriate course of action to take. Ethical conflicts affect not only patients and families, but also the facility's staff, culture, and overall success.

In many healthcare facilities, conflicts are addressed by ethics committees or ethics consultation services (Fox, Myers, and Pearlman 2007; Milmore 2006). When an ethical conflict is recognized by a clinician or an administrator, the involved staff may call upon the organization's ethics mechanism to help address the situation. This reactive approach reflects the traditional manner in which ethics committees or ethics consultation services function when an ethical conflict occurs. While this approach can be helpful in complex and challenging ethical situations, it can be stressful and time consuming for members of the ethics committee or consultation service. In addition, this approach tends to accept the recurrence of ethical conflicts and, in so doing, ignores the underlying system or structure that may have caused the conflict (Forrow, Arnold, and Parker 1993; Nelson 2007).

Because addressing ethical conflicts demands investment of time and places stress on staff, such conflicts are clearly associated with financial costs. Little is known about the costs of ethical conflicts for two reasons. First, any analysis of costs associated with ethical conflicts is complex and does not have a framework that is specific to healthcare ethics. Second, historically, the costs of ethical conflicts were thought to be trivial or were simply an accepted part of the overall costs of delivering healthcare; thus, any analysis was not deemed worthy of the needed effort.

As healthcare executives and managers increasingly focus on balancing quality and cost, exploring the costs of ethical conflicts becomes a logical step in cost-control efforts. In this article, we use five case vignettes of actual ethical situations but with fictitious names to identify and categorize the costs related to ethical conflicts. We then offer recommendations for strategically decreasing costs associated with ethical conflicts in healthcare settings.

CASE VIGNETTES

CASE 1

Eighty-one-year-old Mr. Stanton struggled for years with end-stage chronic obstructive pulmonary disease. Mr. Stanton was admitted to the hospital with bilateral pneumonia. Because of his compromised pulmonary function, he was placed on a ventilator and received an aggressive course of antibiotics. During his hospitalization, he became increasingly disoriented. Despite the gradual clearing of his pneumonia, the medical team was unable to extubate him. As Mr. Stanton's hospitalization continued, the medical team realized that his mental status was unlikely to change and that he had become ventilator dependent.

A week of further assessment confirmed this unfortunate prognosis. Mr. Stanton's wife indicated to the medical team that he would never want to live in such a situation and authorized the removal of the ventilator. Several family members disagreed, but Mrs. Stanton was adamant. These family members threatened to sue if the medical team removed the patient's life-sustaining treatment. The hospital's ethics committee and risk management office were consulted by the medical team because the staff did not know how to proceed. Over the next week, several meetings took place that involved the patient's wife and family members, the medical team and other staff on the case, members of the ethics committee, and the hospital's legal counsel. The decision was reached to remove Mr. Stanton from life-sustaining treatment. He died soon after being extubated.

CASE 2

Mr. Larson was a 63-year-old man who suffered from small-cell lung cancer. He was admitted to the hospital after collapsing on the street. He had not been an inpatient at the hospital despite his cancer, but he had used services at one of the hospital's community clinics. Mr. Larson had received a short course of outpatient chemotherapy, but he frequently missed doctor's appointments and expressed little interest in treatment for cancer. Mr. Larson was divorced and lived alone with several dogs.

Upon admission to the hospital, Mr. Larson was found to be minimally responsive. A CT scan of his brain showed a large metastasis. The medical team pursued further assessment, even though the prognosis was grave. A review of his outpatient chart indicated that he had a few discussions regarding end-of-life issues, but no specific decision was noted. Over the next few days, Mr. Larson became less responsive and his breathing became more difficult. The hospital's social worker was unsuccessful in identifying his next of kin. During several meetings about this case, the medical team debated the treatments to address Mr. Larson's many medical problems. The team finally called the hospital's ethics committee and risk management office for assistance.

After gathering the appropriate patient information, the hospital went to court to obtain a guardian who could make Mr. Larson's healthcare decisions. During this lengthy process, Mr. Larson's health continued to deteriorate. After a guardian was appointed, the decision was made to provide palliative care, including a Do Not Resuscitate order. Mr. Larson died in the hospital four days later. The total cost for several weeks of hospitalization was more than $30,000, but Mr. Larson was uninsured.

CASE 3

Mr. Granger, a 67-year-old veteran, has emphysema, a result of an extended history of smoking. Despite cutting back on the number of cigarettes, he continued to smoke. Following a recent hospital admission for shortness of breath, Mr. Granger was informed by a pulmonary consultant that other than giving him treatment for his symptoms, including 24-hour oxygen support, little more could be done for his illness. Upon discharge to his apartment, Mr. Granger was provided with home oxygen, whose placement was facilitated by the hospital's visiting nurse program. The visiting nurse advised him about the importance of not smoking, which he accepted. During multiple follow-up visits, however, the visiting nurse and the oxygen supplier both noted that he continued to smoke. The director of the visiting nurse program contacted the hospital's ethics committee to discuss the situation.

CASE 4

Despite its fully occupied nursing home that has a long waiting list, a rural critical access hospital and its nursing home were experiencing great financial pressures, which could be the result of the facilities' payer mix dominated by Medicare patients. Mrs. Poison, a prominent 83-year-old citizen in the community, was admitted to the hospital for heart disease and chronic pulmonary ailments. After consultation with Mrs. Poison and her family, the attending physician agreed that she needed nursing home placement.

Mrs. Poison and her family wanted immediate placement in the hospital's nursing home. However, the discharge planner explained that, even though Mrs. Poison was a private-pay patient, she would be put on the waiting list. The family spoke with the nursing home administrator about the situation, reminding him that Mrs. Poison had been a major contributor to the hospital and that she was a higher-revenue-producing private patient. The administrator realized that if he did not act, the family would place Mrs. Poison in a nursing home in the next county. Mrs. Poison was moved up on the waiting list so that she was admitted to the nursing home immediately. At the nursing home, she casually mentioned to a fellow resident the circumstances surrounding her admission. That resident then shared the information with her son, who turned out to be a reporter for the local newspaper. After making several inquiries, the reporter wrote a story, entitled "Money Means Access in Community Nursing Home," alleging unethical admission practices at the nursing home.

The hospital investigated the case and developed a committee made up of members of the hospital's ethics committee and the managers of compliance and human resources.

This committee was charged with reviewing the organization's code of ethics. The hospital also consulted with a public relations firm to help foster its public image in the wake of the negative publicity.

Ms. Penzel, a lean 50-year-old woman, needed a hysterectomy. During the surgery, Dr. Harrison accidentally nicked her lower bowel. The bowel was repaired and assessed to ensure that it was adequately sealed. Ms. Penzel was immediately started on antibiotics to prevent any potential infection from intestinal leakage. There were no postoperative complications; however, Dr. Harrison elected to keep Ms. Penzel as an inpatient for a day longer than planned to watch for any infection and maintain the IV antibiotics.

When Ms. Penzel inquired about the reason for the extended length of stay, Dr. Harrison indicated that he wanted "to play it safe" to make sure the incision was healing properly. Following discharge, Ms. Penzel developed a low-grade fever and chills. She called Dr. Harrison, who then asked her to visit his outpatient office. Dr. Harrison examined her incision site and encouraged her to continue to take the oral antibiotics. Later that day, an operating nurse asked Dr. Harrison how Ms. Penzel took the news about the accidental cut. He told the nurse that he did not tell Ms. Penzel because "she was not harmed" and strongly suggested to the nurse that she "should forget it." The nurse felt conflicted and upset about Dr. Harrison's statement because she believed the patient had the right to know the truth.

After several days, the nurse discussed the situation with her supervisor. A meeting was called with the hospital's ethics committee's consultation team, compliance officer, and risk management office. In a follow-up visit with Dr. Harrison, Ms. Penzel was recovering fine and showed no evidence of infection; she again inquired about her postoperative care. Dr. Harrison told her, "There was a little, accidental nick, but it was taken care of, so all is good." When Ms. Penzel got home, she became more and more upset about the news and decided to contact her lawyer. Her lawyer met with hospital executives, their legal counsel, and Dr. Harrison. A small settlement was reached that included an apology from Dr. Harrison and a review of hospital procedures following an adverse event.

COST ANALYSIS

The case vignettes represent common and often recurring ethical conflicts in healthcare—end-of-life decisions, conflicts of interest, and truth telling following an adverse event. In most of these cases, the staff sought the advice of the facility's ethics committee.

These cases reveal several cost categories related to ethical conflicts—operational costs, legal costs, and marketing and public relations costs. Similar to what Weeks and colleagues (2001) reported regarding recurring medical errors, each cost category includes direct, indirect, and long-term costs associated with the ethical conflict.

OPERATIONAL COSTS

As noted in all the case vignettes, when an ethical conflict occurs, the organization incurs immediate direct costs associated with the time that staff spent on addressing the situation. For example, in Case 1, the uncertainty regarding the patient's end-of-life decision required hospital physicians, nurses, and other staff to spend a considerable amount of time clarifying the patient's or his family's preferences. Similarly, in Case 2, staff spent hours reviewing old records, tracking down outpatient healthcare providers, and going to court—all to determine the best healthcare decision maker for the nonresponsive patient. In addition, these conflicts consumed the time of members of the ethics committee; in four of the five cases presented, ethics consultants helped to guide the situations. The total number of hours expended by these ethics consultants added up, including meeting with the staff involved, the patient, and the family; researching the conflict by reviewing patient records, organizational policies, and relevant literature on the topic; and facilitating and attending meetings.

Indirect costs of these cases include the clinical and administrative staff's time lost, preventing them from seeing other patients or performing other duties while attending to the ethical conflict. For the majority of ethics consultants, performing a consultation is a collateral activity and takes them away from other activities (Fox, Myers, and Pearlman 2007). It has been reported that staff's morale and stress are affected by ethical conflicts (Bischoff, DeTienne, and Quick 1999; Fandray 2000).

Long-term operational costs also result from ethical conflicts or uncertainty. Ethics-related stress can lead to staff burnout and job turnover. Because of the amount of time a staff member puts into dealing with an ethical conflict, the organization may need to not only hire additional staff, but also offer higher wages to meet staffing needs in a limited job market.

LEGAL COSTS

Some ethical conflicts bring about legal and risk management costs. These direct legal costs can include the compensation of legal counsel and risk management personnel (Cases 1, 2, 3, and 5), legal consulting fees (Case 5), deposition and court fees (Case 2), and settlements and payments (Case 5).

Risk management personnel address the ethical conflict by attending meetings, doing research, and conducting investigations. These activities create indirect organizational costs because they decrease the office's efficiency. Any pending legal action will decrease the productivity of risk management personnel and will likely increase their stress.

In addition, ethical conflicts can create long-term risk management costs, such as higher malpractice premiums, a greater allocation of resources to anticipated malpractice or settlement awards, and even higher credit costs (Weeks et al. 2001). Further, the legal ramifications of recurring ethical conflicts could require a need for additional risk management staff.

MARKETING AND PUBLIC RELATIONS COSTS

Direct marketing and public relations costs are most clearly evident in Case 4. These costs accrued as a result of the organization's efforts to rectify the action taken by its nursing home administrator. Clearly, containing negative publicity consumes public relations personnel and marketing resources. As was the situation for the nursing home of a critical access hospital in Case 4, when facilities have limited in-house public relations resources to address ethical dilemmas that have gone public, outside consultants may need to be hired. Public relations firms often charge a higher rate for a rapidly unfolding crisis because it can be costly to quickly research the issues at hand, strategize, and execute a sound plan.

Indirect costs include all the resources necessary to rebuild, through various initiatives, the facility's image and the community's perception. Such activities will divert personnel, including the executive team and trustees, from other responsibilities. Staff morale may be adversely affected, which can later make recruiting efforts more challenging. Patient satisfaction assessments can also be negatively affected by the presence of ethical conflicts.

The long-term impact of an unethical action is a product of the negative public perception. Such a perception potentially affects self-referrals, which in turn could decrease the facility's market share and lead to its closing; this is the situation for the small, rural nursing home in Case 4. In addition, philanthropic support to the organization, including financial donations and volunteer hours, could be adversely affected. Importantly, redirecting earmarked marketing resources to reduce negative publicity in the wake of an ethics crisis may result in the halting of advertising or other initiatives aimed at promoting more profitable service lines, such as oncology and cardiology. Reallocation of marketing resources may minimize the public backlash, but the missed opportunities to promote key service lines may be especially damaging to facilities that seek a more diverse payer mix. Note that long-term costs are likely incurred long after the ethical issue has passed, as losing the trust of stakeholders is a difficult, long, and expensive event from which to recover.

DISCUSSION

Ethical conflicts are common phenomena that have significant cost implications for healthcare organizations. Although the vignettes represent composite cases, our experience indicates that the situations in each case are not unfamiliar to healthcare staff. Our analysis suggests that organizations have a financial incentive, in addition to philosophical reasons, to focus on decreasing the occurrence of ethical conflicts because such cases account for significant potential legal, marketing, and operational costs (see table 8.2). This analysis is not an attempt to precisely quantify the cost of each ethical conflict; it merely identifies the potential cost implications. Research reinforces the argument that ethical conflicts have an impact on organizational and health delivery costs (Arthur Andersen 1999; Veit 2001; Fandray 2000; Spiller 2000; Bischoff, DeTienne, and Quick 1999; Kraman and Hamm 1999; Verschoor 1999; Nickell 1995; Vincent, Young, and Phillips 1994; Heilicser, Meltzer, and Siegler 2000; LRN 2006).

Even though reservations exist about focusing on cost issues related to evaluating ethics activities (Mills, Tereskerz, and Davis 2005), understanding the cost ramifications of ethical conflicts is important. In fact, we agree with the point made by Bacchetta and Fins (1997, 452): "We find the dearth of economic arguments on this issue both puzzling and misguided given the potential cost savings associated with an effective

TABLE 8.2 POTENTIAL COSTS OF ETHICAL CONFLICTS

Operations cost categories	Direct costs	• Staff time • Ethics consultant's time
	Indirect costs	• Staff and consultant's time diverted from patient care and/or other activities • Staff and consultant's stress • Decreased staff morale
	Long-term costs	• Staff burnout • Staff turnover • Additional staff needed
Legal cost categories	Direct costs	• Risk management staff time • Legal fees • Court fees • Settlement costs
	Indirect costs	• Staff work diverted from other activities • Staff stress
	Long-term costs	• Higher malpractice costs • Budget adjustments for settlements and awards • Additional staff needed
Public relations cost categories	Direct costs	• Public relations time • Public relations consultant's costs • Advertising costs
	Indirect costs	• Public image needs to be rebuilt • Staff work diverted • Staff morale and stress
	Long-term costs	• Negative public image • Loss of self-referrals and market share • Decreased philanthropic support

ethics program and the prevailing concern about cost containment." Reducing ethical conflicts, and realizing that action has potential for cost savings, should not be overlooked by healthcare organizations.

After identifying the cost categories affected by ethical conflicts, we wanted to consider the impact of those categories in a competitive environment. We explored the theoretical correlation between organizational costs and an ethical conflict along four determinants of corporate performance—wages, price, efficiency, and cost of capital (Nickell 1995). Figure 8.5 demonstrates the impact of a conflict on the organization's overall profit margin. The rate of litigation is probably low in relation to the overall number of ethical conflicts. However, when litigation does occur as a result of the conflict, many costs can be incurred that negatively affect the facility's budget. These costs include expenses for legal counsel, risk management investigation, litigation defense, and any settlements and awards (Kavaler and Spiegel 1997; Weeks et al. 2001).

On the other hand, when ethical conflicts are minimized, an organization can obtain lower interest rates for financing because the bank considers it less exposed to ethical risks (Weeks et al. 2001). Operational costs are affected by decreased staff efficiency and increased staff turnover, which possibly necessitate additional staff and higher wages. The facility's poor reputation will likely decrease the number of self-referrals as well as the price for services, because a facility with better reputation has a greater degree of market power, especially in a competitive environment (Weeks and Mills 2003; Weeks and Bagian 2003). Figure 8.5 emphasizes that the identified cost categories affected by ethical conflicts are not insignificant and that conflicts can ultimately lessen the organization's profit margin.

RECOMMENDATIONS

Most facilities rely on a reactive ethics consultation program or ethics committee to address ethical dilemmas. Using a quantitative approach, Bacchetta and Fins (1997) found that effective ethics consultation may yield economic benefits to a healthcare organization. Despite the potential financial advantages of a traditional reactive consultation model (Daly 2000), a *preventive approach* to ethical conflicts should be considered.

Several studies have demonstrated that a proactive ethics consultation approach, involving intensive care unit patients and terminally ill patients, either reduces or prevents organizational costs (Dowdy, Robertson, and Bander 1998; Schneiderman et al. 2003). We suggest that such a strategy should be applied broadly throughout the facility to stem ethical conflicts, thereby enhancing the organization's quality-of-care and cost-effectiveness efforts. The basic premise here is to understand the cause of conflicts and to enact policies or guidelines that are likely to reduce their occurrence or mitigate their effects, in turn decreasing the resulting costs.

We suggest two practical strategies for decreasing ethical conflicts. First, after an ethics committee or ethics consultation program responds to a conflict, as was done in four out of the five case vignettes, the committee should facilitate a process with the involved staff to identify the underlying causes of the conflict and take corrective

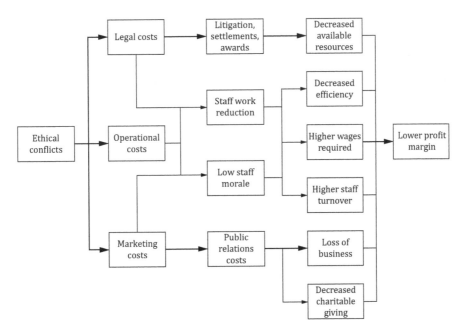

Figure 8.5 Effects on Organizational Performance, by Cost
Categories

actions to eliminate or decrease recurrence. For example, performing a root cause
analysis (RCA) would help to determine why the conflict occurred and what can
be done to prevent it from happening again. The RCA process focuses on improvement—and when needed, on redesigning systems and processes—rather than on the
individuals involved in the conflict (National Center for Patient Safety 2007).

Second, the organization should proactively identify from various areas in the facility
those ethical conflicts that have been recurring. Because the number of ethical conflicts
addressed by ethics committees (see Fox, Myers, and Pearlman 2007; Milmore 2006)
is probably only a small percentage of the actual number of conflicts faced by facilities,
a proactive approach is needed. By "recurring ethical conflicts," we mean those situations that repeatedly raise the same basic ethical concerns, such as disagreements or
uncertainties about end-of-life decision making, about full disclosure of information
following an adverse event, and about a patient's demand for a clinician who is from
a specific ethnic group. A recurring ethical case involves different patients, at different times, and in different settings, but it brings up the same kind of conflict. Once
the recurring conflict is identified, an ethical practice protocol should be developed
that provides guidance for addressing the conflict. The guidance can help prevent the
situation from becoming a conflict (Halloran et al. 1995). For example, proactively

reviewing end-of-life conflicts, as in Cases 1 and 2, could lead to an organization-wide effort to improve the staff's use of advance care decision-making documents (Tierney et al. 2001). Such a proactive approach has been suggested by several researchers (McCullough 1998; Forrow, Arnold, and Parker 1993; Chervenak and McCullough 2004; McCullough 2005; Nelson 2007).

The proactive approach is based on five basic steps (Nelson 2007):

1. Identify recurring ethical issues that create conflict or uncertainty.

2. Study the issues in a systematic, system-oriented manner.

3. Develop ethical practice protocols to guide clinicians and executives when those issues arise again.

4. Propagate the protocols throughout the organization's culture so that all staff are aware of the guidelines and the rationale behind them.

5. Review whether the protocols are adequately addressing and decreasing the occurrence of ethical issues.

This proactive, preventive approach can be used in various settings and situations. For example, a member of the ethics committee could meet with the organization's patient safety officer to ask, "What are the recurring ethical issues you and your staff encounter that disrupt the quality of care by creating uncertainty or conflict?" (Nelson et al., in press). The issues identified and prioritized could then be systematically and thoughtfully discussed with all appropriate parties, leading to the development of an ethically grounded, proactive protocol. Once the protocols or guidelines are shared throughout the organization, the extent of uncertainty can be decreased.

Even though this process may seem arduous, it creates an environment of increased ethical certainty and staff satisfaction because the process hinders the occurrence of stressful, time-consuming, and costly ethical conflicts. To the degree that this process can prevent short-term and long-term costs, the healthcare organization will reap a positive return if it invests in such a proactive, preventive approach to responding to ethical conflicts (Weeks 2002).

CONCLUSION

Our analysis suggests that healthcare organizations have a financial incentive to focus on decreasing the occurrence of ethical conflicts because such conflicts can account for significant legal, operational, and marketing and public relations costs. Despite the economic value of effective, reactive ethics committee activities, organizations should develop strategies for decreasing and preventing conflicts because of the potential related costs. This proactive strategy requires a shift in focus, from merely reacting to moving upstream—that is, understanding the root causes of conflicts and employing approaches that are designed to reduce or inhibit conflicts and hence costs. Such an effort has the potential of enhancing the organization's overall culture and ultimately contributing to its success.

REFERENCES

Arthur Andersen Co. 1999. "Ethical Concerns and Reputation Risk Management: A Study of Leading U.K. Companies." London: London Business School.

Bacchetta, M. D., and J. J. Fins. 1997. The Economics of Clinical Ethics Programs: A Quantitative Justification." *Cambridge Quarterly of Healthcare Ethics* 6: 451–60.

Bischoff, S. J., K. B. DeTienne, and B. Quick, 1999. "Effects of Ethics Stress on Employee Burnout and Fatigue: An Empirical Investigation." *Journal of Health & Human Resources Administration* 21: 512–32.

Chervenak, F. A., and L. B. McCullough. 2004. "An Ethical Framework for Identifying, Preventing, and Managing Conflicts Confronting Leaders of Academic Health Centers." *Academic Medicine* 79 (11): 1056–61.

Daly, G. 2000. "Ethics and Economics." *Nursing Economics* 18 (4): 194–201.

Dowdy, M. D., C. Robertson, and J. A. Bander. 1998. "A Study of Proactive Ethics Consultation for Critically and Terminally Ill Patients with Extended Lengths of Stay." *Critical Care Medicine* 26 (2): 252–59.

Fandray, D. 2000. "The Ethical Company." *Workforce* 79 (12): 74–77.

Forrow, L., R. M. Arnold, and L. S. Parker. 1993 "Preventive Ethics: Expanding the Horizons of Clinical Ethics." *Journal of Clinical Ethics* 4 (4): 287–94.

Fox, E., S. Myers, and R. A. Pearlman. 2007. "Ethics Consultation in United States Hospitals: A National Survey." *American Journal of Bioethics* 7 (2): 12–25.

Halloran, S. D., G. W. Starkey, P. A. Burke, G. Steele, and R. A. Forse. 1995. "An Educational Intervention in the Surgical Intensive Care Unit to Improve Ethical Decisions." *Surgery* 118 (2): 294–99.

Heilicser, B. J., D. Meltzer, and M. Siegler. 2000. "The Effect of Clinical Medical Ethics Consultation on Healthcare Costs." *The Journal of Clinical Ethics* 11 (1): 31–38.

Kavaler, F., and A. Spiegel. 1997. *Risk Management in Health Care Institutions: A Strategic Approach.* Sudbury, MA: Jones and Bartlett.

Kraman, S. S., and G. Hamm. 1999. "Risk Management: Extreme Honesty May Be the Best Policy." *Annals of Internal Medicine* 131 (12): 963–67.

LRN. 2006. "New Research Indicates Ethical Corporate Cultures Impact the Ability to Attract, Retain and Ensure Productivity Among U.S. Workers." [Online article; retrieved 8/31/07.] www.lrn.com/about_lrn/media_room/press_releases/263.

McCullough, L. B. 1998. "Preventive Ethics, Managed Practice, and the Hospital Ethics Committee as a Resource for Physician Executives." *HEC Forum* 10 (2): 136–51.

_____. 2005. "Practicing Preventive Ethics—the Keys to Avoiding Ethical Conflicts in Health Care." *Physician Executive* 31 (2): 18–21.

Mills, A., P. Tereskerz, and W. Davis. 2005. "Is Evaluating Ethics Consultation on the Basis of Cost a Good Idea?" *Cambridge Quarterly of Healthcare Ethics* 14: 57–64.

Milmore, D. 2006. "Hospital Ethics Committees: A Survey in Upstate New York," *HEC Forum* 18 (3): 222–44.

National Center for Patient Safety. 2007. "Root Cause Analysis." [Online article; retrieved 7/19/07.] www.va.gov/NCPS/rca.html.

Nelson, W. A. 2007. "Decreasing Ethical Conflicts." *Healthcare Executive* 22 (2): 36–38.

Nelson, W. A., J. Neily, P. Mills, and W. B. Weeks. In press. "Collaboration of Ethics and Patient Safety Programs: Opportunities to Promote Quality and Safety." *HEC Forum.*

Nickell, S. 1995. *The Performance of Companies: Mitsui Lectures in Economics.* Oxford, UK: Blackwell Publishers.

Schneiderman, L. J., T. Gilmer, H. D. Teetzel, D. O. Dugan, J. Blustein, R. Cranford, K. B. Briggs, G. I. Komatsu, P. Goodman-Crews, F. Cohn, and E. W. Young. 2003. "Effect of Ethics Consultations on Nonbeneficial Life-Sustaining Treatments in the Intensive Care Unit." *JAMA* 290 (9): 1166–72.

Spiller, R. 2000. "Ethical Business and Investment: A Model for Business and Society." *Journal of Business Ethics* 27: 149–60.

Tierney, W. M., P. R. Dexter, G. P. Gramel spacher, A. J. Perkins, X. H. Zhou, and F. D. Wolinsky. 2001. "The Effect of Discussions About Advance Directives on Patients' Satisfaction with Primary Care." *Journal of General Internal Medicine* 16: 32–40.

Veit, L. 2001. "Ethical Matters." *Credit Union Management* 24 (6): 18–20.

Verschoor, C. C. 1999. "Corporate Performance Is Closely Linked to a Strong Ethical Commitment." *Business and Society Review* 104 (4): 407–15.

Vincent, C., M. Young, and A. Phillips. 1994. "Why Do People Sue Doctors? A Study of Patients and Relatives Taking Legal Action." *Lancet* 343: 1609–13.

Weeks, W. B. 2002. "Quality Improvement as an Investment." *Quality Management in Health Care* 10 (3): 55–64.

Weeks, W. B., J. Waldron, T. Foster, P. Mills, and E. Stalhandske. 2001. "The Organizational Costs of Preventable Medical Errors." *Journal on Quality Improvement* 27 (10): 533–39.

Weeks, W. B., and J. P. Bagian. 2003. "Making a Business Case for Patient Safety." *Joint Commission Journal on Quality and Safety* 29 (1): 51–54.

Weeks, W. B., and P. D. Mills. 2003. "Reduction in Patient Enrollment in the Veterans Healthcare Administration After Media Coverage of Adverse Medical Events." *Joint Commission Journal on Quality and Safety* 29 (12): 652–58.

PRACTITIONER APPLICATION

Les MacLeod, EdD, LFACHE, professor of health management and policy, University of New Hampshire, Durham

As economic forces exert growing pressure on the U.S. healthcare system for more value-based services, practitioners everywhere are finding themselves faced with the difficult and ongoing task of balancing costs and quality in ways that are both clinically acceptable and economically efficient. Associated factors, such as increased operating costs, a competitive healthcare marketplace, life-prolonging advancements in medical technology, growing workforce shortages, and an aging population, are making this task even more important and challenging. In addition, a better informed and engaged consumer population continues to exert growing social and political pressure for a more affordable, safe, and transparent delivery system. Such diverse and complex developments provide fertile grounds for potential growth in both the number and extent of ethical conflicts within various healthcare settings. The health-care organization's ability to effectively deal with these ethical issues on a systemwide level will more than likely attract added visibility and take on greater importance in the immediate future.

In this well-referenced article, Nelson, Weeks, and Campfield make a persuasive argument for healthcare organizations to transition from a historically reactive, case-specific response to ethical issues to a proactive and intentional systems approach. Through case vignettes, the authors illustrate that while ethical conflicts are by nature case-specific, these conflicts share a thread of commonalities, which can then be used to formulate a management methodology that is responsive to both quality of care and cost containment. The authors' reasoning makes sense on a number of important levels. Understanding ethics-related expenditures is qualitatively the right thing to do, is likely to be cost effective in the long run, and ultimately makes sound business sense from both an internal and external relationships perspective.

In addition, the authors provide a conceptual framework for bringing sharply into focus the many and varied costs associated with common ethical conflicts. The framework is a useful tool that can help to identify and categorize a host of obvious and not so obvious costs that can be potentially reduced or eliminated through a more comprehensive internal ethical conflicts management system. The authors also shed light on the impact of ethical conflicts on a number of less obvious, and, as a result, often overlooked, collateral factors such as culture; associated opportunity costs; and employee stress, burnout, and turnover.

The article lays out a very practical, goal-directed process for operationalizing throughout an organization a core principle—the time-tested "ounce of prevention" maxim. Using root cause analysis, and recommending the development of ethical practice protocols, the authors outline a systems initiative that has logical progression, is efficient in design, and is easy and inexpensive to implement. It is a process that can very well lead to and facilitate improved and/or redesigned systems. This can, in turn, reduce the occurrence of ethical conflicts along with many kinds of associated economic costs and negative operational intangibles.

REFLECTIONS ON THE READING SELECTIONS

We offer the following editorial commentary on the reading selections.

1. A common error that many make is with HIPAA. In the article by Gray and Christiansen, several times in the paper they incorrectly state it as HIPPA when it should be listed as HIPAA.

2. The article by Gray and Christiansen discusses both legal and ethical principles that should guide healthcare organizations. We challenge you to reach out to your own healthcare organization to identify the ethical guidelines and policies regarding ethical dilemmas.

3. Healthcare organizations are faced with the competing interests of quality care and cost containment, as discussed in the article by Nelson et al. Although it may seem harsh to associate costs with ethical dilemmas, it is necessary to prioritize areas within healthcare that can be improved to reduce the risks with ethical conflicts.

APPLICATION AND SYNTHESIS

"Only one rule in medical ethics need concern you: that action on your part which best conserves the interest of your patient."— *Martin H. Fisher, Get Real Health president and founding partner* (Quote Garden, 2014)

QUESTIONS FOR DISCUSSION

1. What unique challenges do healthcare organizations face when marketing online?

2. List some potential conflicts that may occur with medical marketing.

3. Should healthcare organizations market? Why or why not? Be specific.

4. What benefits do potential patients obtain from marketing?

5. How do codes of ethics help when it comes to developing medical marketing materials?

6. Can you think of examples of unethical medical marketing as well as ethical medical marketing?

SUMMARY OF MAIN POINTS

After reading this chapter, you should be able to:

√ Discuss codes of ethics (p. 227–229)
√ Identify potential ethical workplace conflicts (p. 239–244)
√ Discuss legal and ethical marketing issues for healthcare organizations (p. 236)

COMPREHENSION ASSESSMENT

1. List and discuss the four pillars of medical ethics.

2. Identify specific examples of direct marketing guidelines for marketers.

3. Identify and discuss three types of costs that occur with ethical conflicts.

4. Discuss the two practical strategies that were suggested to decrease ethical conflicts.

CONCLUSION

In this chapter, we discussed ethics and medical marketing. The topic of ethics is extremely important in healthcare, so we encourage you to continue to think ethically within your organizations.

We hope that this book has provided an opportunity for you to begin to explore marketing issues for healthcare organizations. With changing governmental healthcare legislation, it is unclear what changes may occur within the healthcare industry. However, whatever form healthcare legislation may take, it is certain that healthcare will continue to be patient-centered. This means that healthcare administrators should continue to seek innovative solutions to improving the patient experience.

REFERENCES

American Medical Association. *Code of medical ethics*. Retrieved from https://www.ama-assn.org/about-us/code-medical-ethics

Quote Garden. *Quotations on medical subjects*. Retrieved from http://www.quotegarden.com/medical.html.

University of Ottawa. *Basic ethical principles*. Retrieved from https://www.med.uottawa.ca/sim/data/Ethics_e.htm.

IMAGE CREDITS

AUTHOR BIOS

Dr. Barbara Ross Wooldridge is a professor of marketing at The University of Texas at Tyler. She holds a PhD from Louisiana State University, an MPS from the Statler School of Hotel Management, Cornell University, and a BFA in Mass Communications from James Madison University. She has both an academic and a professional background in Marketing. She has extensive experience in international and services marketing, having worked in Kenya and the Seychelles. She has spent the last five years immersed in researching the healthcare field and has taught for UT Tyler's online MBA in Healthcare Management and Executive MBA in Healthcare Management. She has taught basic healthcare marketing, special topics in healthcare, and healthcare in the

global context. She has served as an expert witness in a medical/marketing case. Her primary research focus is services marketing and customer satisfaction. She has been published in such journals as the *Journal of Business Research*, *Journal of Consumer Marketing*, *Journal of Managerial Issues*, *Corporate Communications: An International Journal*, and others. She has been active in the Society for Marketing Advances (SMA) since 1996 and is a faculty associate in the American College of Healthcare Executives (ACHE). She was named a 2013 University of Texas System Regents' Outstanding Teacher.

Contact information: brosswoo@uttyler.edu

Dr. Kerri M. Camp is an associate professor of marketing at The University of Texas at Tyler. She holds a PhD from Texas Tech University, an MBA in Management from Golden Gate University, and a BBA in Marketing from Texas A&M University. She has over seven years of industry experience in healthcare administration and marketing consulting for healthcare organizations, and she served on multiple healthcare organization boards and advisory committees. She has been an invited columnist for The Daily Sentinel, a

media consultant for local CBS and NBC news, and a guest speaker for numerous state and local organizations. Dr. Camp has taught several marketing courses at the undergraduate and graduate level, including Health Care Marketing and Special Topics in Healthcare for UT Tyler's online MBA in Healthcare Management and Executive MBA in Healthcare Management. Her primary research focus is healthcare management issues and, in particular, patient satisfaction and value in healthcare. She has been published in the *Journal of Business Research*, *Journal of Retail and Consumer Services*, *Family Business Review*, *Journal of Applied Management and Entrepreneurship*, *Information Systems Frontiers*, and others. She is a faculty associate at the American College of Healthcare Executives (ACHE) and was the keynote speaker for ACHE East Texas Chapter in 2016 on Creating Value in the Patient Experience—Applying the Drivers of Consumer Satisfaction and Loyalty. She received the 2017 Provost's Excellence in Teaching Award.

Contact information: kcamp@uttyler.edu

CPSIA information can be obtained
at www.ICGtesting.com
Printed in the USA
BVHW061208080722
641448BV00001B/10

9 781516 514267